THE BIRTH OF A NEW PHYSICS

Birth of a New Physics is a subject close to the professional heart of I. BERNARD COHEN of Harvard University. The historic, scientific, and cultural implications of Sir Isaac Newton's great discoveries have been a special interest of Professor Cohen for years. Author of *Franklin and Newton* (1956) and editor of *Isaac Newton's Papers on Natural Philosophy* (1957), Professor Cohen has spent the last four summers reading everything he could find by Newton or about Newton in the manuscript archives of the great academies of England, Holland, France, and Italy. Eventually his studies will culminate in the first critical and variorum edition of Newton's *Principia Mathematica* ever to be published.

Professor Cohen was born in Far Rockaway, New York, in 1914. He received his bachelor of science degree in mathematics, *cum laude*, in 1937, from Harvard and did graduate work in physics, astronomy, and the history of science at the same university. He received his Ph.D. in the history of science in 1947. He has been a member of the Harvard science faculty since 1942 and now is Professor of the History of Science.

For six years Professor Cohen was managing editor and for another six years editor (1953–59) of *Isis,* the official quarterly journal of the History of Science Society. He is the author of *Science, Servant of Man* (1948) and other books and has contributed articles to the *Journal of the History of Ideas, Isis,* and *Scientific American* and to French, Italian, and Spanish publications. He has been a special lecturer at University College, London, and at the Sorbonne in Paris, Oxford, Florence, and numerous American universities. He is vice-president of the History of Science Society in the United States and was delegate to the Ninth International Congress of the History of Science (Barcelona-Madrid).

Away from his typewriter and archives, Professor Cohen is an ardent traveler and tower climber, an enthusiasm shared by his young daughter. (Once he almost was wedged in the spiral stairs of England's York Minster.) Photographing castles and boats, especially fishing boats, is another hobby.

Professor Cohen's research in the relation of scientific ideas to society is particularly pertinent in the educational ferment America now is experiencing. In the history of science he sees "a unity of *all* human creativity and a medium in which science can regain the humanizing dimensions so often lost in purely formal presentations."

The Birth
of a New Physics

I. BERNARD COHEN

Published by
Anchor Books
Doubleday & Company, Inc.
Garden City, New York
1960

Available to secondary school
students and teachers through
Wesleyan University Press Incorporated
Columbus 16, Ohio

To
FRANCES BERNARD COHEN
One of the generation
that will study science
in the new mode inaugurated
by the P.S.S.C.

Library of Congress Catalog Card Number 60–5918

THE SCIENCE STUDY SERIES

The Science Study Series offers to students and to the general public the writing of distinguished authors on the most stirring and fundamental topics of physics, from the smallest known particles to the whole universe. Some of the books tell of the role of physics in the world of man, his technology and civilization. Others are biographical in nature, telling the fascinating stories of the great discoverers and their discoveries. All the authors have been selected both for expertness in the fields they discuss and for ability to communicate their special knowledge and their own views in an interesting way. The primary purpose of these books is to provide a survey of physics within the grasp of the young student or the layman. Many of the books, it is hoped, will encourage the reader to make his own investigations of natural phenomena.

These books are published as part of a fresh approach to the teaching and study of physics. At the Massachusetts Institute of Technology during 1956 a group of physicists, high school teachers, journalists, apparatus designers, film producers, and other specialists organized the Physical Science Study Committee, now operating as a part of Educational Services Incorporated, Watertown, Massachusetts. They pooled their knowledge and experience toward the design and creation of aids to the learning of physics. Initially their effort was supported by the National Science Foundation, which has continued to aid the program. The Ford Foundation, the Fund for the Advancement of Education, and the Alfred P. Sloan Foundation have also given support. The Committee is creating a textbook, an extensive film series, a laboratory guide, especially designed apparatus, and a teacher's source book for a new integrated secondary school physics program which is undergoing continuous evaluation with secondary school teachers.

The Series is guided by a Board of Editors, consisting of Paul F. Brandwein, the Conservation Foundation and Harcourt, Brace and Company; John H. Durston, Educational Services Incorporated; Francis L. Friedman, Massachusetts Institute of Technology; Samuel A. Goudsmit, Brookhaven National Laboratory; Bruce F. Kingsbury, Educational Services Incorporated; Philippe LeCorbeiller, Harvard University; Gerard Piel, *Scientific American;* and Herbert S. Zim, Simon and Schuster, Inc.

FOREWORD

The purpose of this book is not to present a "popular" history of science, nor even to display for the general reader some of the recent results of research in the history of science. Rather the intention is to explore one aspect of that great scientific revolution which occurred during the sixteenth and seventeenth centuries, to clarify certain fundamental aspects of the development of modern science. One important theme is the effect of the closely knit structure of the physical sciences on the formation of a science of motion. Since the seventeenth century, again and again we have seen that a major modification in any one part of the physical sciences must eventually produce changes throughout; another consequence is the general impossibility of testing or proving a scientific statement in isolation or fully by itself, each test being rather a verification of the particular proposition under discussion plus the whole system of physical science.

The chief, and perhaps unique, property of modern science is its dynamic aspect, the way in which changes constantly occur. Unfortunately, the needs of logical presentation in elementary textbooks and general works on science prevent the student and reader from gaining a true idea of this particular dynamic property. Hence another of the major aims of this book is to try to indicate the penetrating force and deep effect that a single idea may have in altering the whole structure of science.

I should like to acknowledge my intellectual debt to Professor Alexandre Koyré of the Ecole Pratique des

Hautes Etudes (Paris) and the Institute for Advanced Study (Princeton), our master in the scholarly art of conceptual analysis. Professor Marjorie Hope Nicolson of Columbia University has made us aware of the vast intellectual significance of the "new astronomy" and particularly Galileo's telescopic discoveries. I have, to my great joy and profit over more than a decade, discussed many of these questions with Professor Marshall Clagett of the University of Wisconsin. I have a special obligation to Stillman Drake, who has been more than ordinarily generous in permitting me to see his unpublished Galilean studies, in answering questions, and in giving the typescript of this book a critical reading. Above all, I gladly record my enthusiasm for the Physical Science Study Committee of Educational Services Incorporated (chiefly Professors Jerrold Zacharias and Francis Friedman of M.I.T.) under whose auspices this book was conceived. I am conscious of the privilege of being allowed to have a small share in this great enterprise of reforming the teaching of physics on the secondary-school level. It is hard to find adequate words to express my obligation to the staff of the P.S.S.C. (notably Bruce Kingsbury) which in every way facilitated each step along the way of preparing the book. In particular, I found in John H. Durston a sympathetic editor whose aid reduced my own labor to manageable proportions.

I am grateful to the publishers who have granted permission to quote from published material. The specific books are cited in the Guide to Further Reading at the end of this book.

I.B.C.

CONTENTS

CHAPTER 1

The Physics of a Moving Earth

Odd as it may seem, most people's views about motion are part of a system of physics that was proposed more than 2000 years ago and was experimentally shown to be inadequate at least 1400 years ago. It is a fact that presumably well-educated men and women tend even today to think about the physical world as if the earth were at rest, rather than in motion. By this I do not mean that such people really believe the earth is at rest; if questioned, they will reply that of course they "know" that the earth rotates once a day about its axis and at the same time moves in a great yearly orbit around the sun. Yet when it comes to explaining certain common physical events, these same people are not able to tell you how it is that these everyday phenomena can happen, as we see they do, on a moving earth. In particular, these misunderstandings of physics tend to center on the problem of falling objects, on the general concept of motion. Thus we may see exemplified the old precept, "To ignore motion is to ignore nature."

Where Will It Fall?

In his inability to deal with questions of motion in relation to a moving earth, the average person is in the same position as some of the greatest scientists of the past, which may be a source of considerable comfort to

him. The major difference is, however, that for the
scientist of the past the inability to resolve these questions was a sign of his time, whereas for the modern man
such inability is, alas, a badge of ignorance. Characteristic of these problems is a woodcut of the seventeenth
century (Plate I) showing a cannon pointing up in the
air. Observe the question that is asked, *"Retombera-
t-il?"* (Will it fall back down again?) If the earth is at
rest, there is no doubt that the cannon ball fired straight
up in the air would eventually come straight down again
into the cannon. But will it on a moving earth? And if
it will, why?

In a general way let us examine all the arguments. If
supporters of the theory that the earth may move con-
tended that the air must move along with the earth, and
that an arrow shot up into the air would be carried along
with the moving air and earth, the opponents had a ready
reply: Even if the air could be supposed to move—a
difficult supposition since there is no apparent cause for
the air to move with the earth—would not the air move
very much more slowly than the earth since it is so very
different in substance and in quality? And even so
would not, therefore, the arrow be left behind? And
what of the high winds that a man in a tower should feel?

In order to see these problems in sharper relief, let us
for a moment ignore the earth itself. After all, the average man and woman may very well reply: I may not be
able to explain how a ball dropped from a tower will
strike the ground at the foot of the tower even though the
earth is moving. But I do know that a dropped ball de-
scends vertically, and I do know that the earth is in motion. So there *must* be some explanation, even if I am not
aware of it.

Let us, then, deal with another situation altogether.
Let us simply assume that we are able to construct some
kind of vehicle which will move very quickly—so quickly
indeed that its speed will be approximately 20 miles per

second. An experimenter stands at the end of this vehicle, on an observation platform of the last car if it happens to be a train. While the train is rushing ahead at a speed of 20 miles a second, he takes an iron ball weighing about a pound from his pocket and throws it vertically into the air to a height of 16 feet. The ascent takes about one second, and it takes another second for the ball to come down. How far has the man at the end of the train moved? Since his speed is 20 miles per second, he will have traveled 40 miles from the spot where he threw the ball into the air.

Like the man who drew the picture of a cannon firing a ball up into the air, we ask: Where will it fall? Will the ball come down to strike the track at or very near the place from which it was thrown? Or, will the ball somehow or other manage to come down so near the hands of the man who threw it that he will be able to catch it, even though his train is moving at a speed of 20 miles per second? If you reply that the ball will strike the track some miles behind the train, then you clearly do not understand the physics of the earth in motion. But, if you believe that the man on the back of the train will catch the ball, you will then have to face the question: What force makes the ball move forward with a speed of 20 miles a second even though the man throwing the ball gave it an upward force and not a force along the track? (Those who may be concerned about the possibilities of air friction can imagine the experiment as being conducted inside a car of the train.)

The belief that a ball thrown straight upward from the moving train will continue to move along a straight line straight up and straight down so as to strike the track at a point far behind the train, is closely related to another belief about moving objects. Both are part of that system of physics of about 2000 years ago. Let us examine this second problem for a moment, because it happens that the same people who do not understand how objects can appear to fall vertically downward on a moving earth are also not entirely sure what happens when objects of different weight fall. Everyone is aware, of course, that the falling of a body in air depends upon its shape. This can be easily demonstrated if you make a parachute of a handkerchief, knotting the four corners of the handkerchief to four pieces of string and then tying all four pieces of string together to a small weight. Roll this parachute into a ball and throw it up into the air and you will observe that it will float gently downward. But now make it into a ball again, take a piece of silk thread and tie it around the handkerchief and weight so that the handkerchief cannot open in the air, and, as you will observe, the same object will now plummet to earth. But what of objects of the same shape but of different weight? Suppose you were to go to the top of a high tower, or to the third story of a house, and that you were to drop from that height two objects of identical shape, spherical balls, one weighing 10 pounds and the other one pound. Which would strike the ground first? And how much sooner would it strike? If the relation between the two weights, in this case a factor of ten to one, makes a difference, would the same difference in time of fall be observed if the weights were respectively 10 pounds and 100 pounds? And what if they were 1 milligram and 10 milligrams?

Alternative Answers

The usual progression of knowledge of physics goes something like this: First, there is a belief that if 1- and 2-pound balls are dropped simultaneously, the 2-pound ball will strike the ground first, and that it will take the 1-pound ball just twice as long to reach the ground as it did the 2-pound ball. Then follows a stage of greater sophistication, in which the student presumably has learned from an elementary textbook that the previous conclusion is wholly unwarranted, and that the "true" answer is that they will both strike at the same time no matter what their respective weights. The first answer may be called the "Aristotelian view," because it accords with the principles that the Greek philosopher Aristotle formulated in physics about 400 years before the beginning of the Christian Era. The second we may call the "elementary textbook" view, because it is to be found in many such books. Sometimes it is even said that this second view was "proved" in the sixteenth century by the Italian scientist Galileo Galilei. A typical version of this story is that Galileo "caused balls of different sizes and materials to be dropped at the same instant from the top of the Leaning Tower of Pisa. They [his friends and associates] saw the balls start together and fall together, and heard them strike the ground together. Some were convinced; others returned to their rooms to consult the books of Aristotle, discussing the evidence."

Both the Aristotelian and the "elementary textbook" views are wrong, as has been known by experiment for at least 1400 years. Let us go back to the sixth century when Joannes Philoponus (or John the Grammarian), a Byzantine scholar, was studying this question. Philoponus argued that experience contradicts the commonly held views of falling. Adopting what we would call a rather "modern" attitude, he said that an argument based on "actual observation" is much more effective than "any sort of verbal argument." Here is his argument based on experiment:

"For if you let fall from the same height two weights of which one is many times as heavy as the other, you will see that the ratio of the times required for the motion does not depend on the ratio of the weights, but that the difference in time is a very small one. And so, if the difference in the weights is not considerable, that is, if one is, let us say, double the other, there will be no difference, or else an imperceptible difference, in time, though the difference in weight is by no means negligible, with one body weighing twice as much as the other."

In this statement, we find experimental evidence that the "Aristotelian" view is wrong because objects differing greatly in weight, or those which differ in weight by a factor of two, will strike the ground almost at the same time. But observe that Philoponus also suggests that the "elementary textbook" view is incorrect, because he has found that bodies of different weight fall from the same height in different times. One millennium later the Flemish engineer, physicist, and mathematician Simon Stevin performed a similar experiment. His account reads:

"The experience against Aristotle is the following: Let us take (as the very learned Mr. Jan Cornets de Groot, most industrious investigator of the secrets of Nature, and myself have done) two spheres of lead, the one ten times larger and heavier than the other, and drop them together from a height of 30 feet onto a board or something on which they give a perceptible sound. Then it will be found that the lighter will not be ten times longer on its way than the heavier, but that they fall together onto the board so simultaneously that their two sounds seem to be one and the same rap."

Stevin was obviously more interested in proving Aristotle wrong than in trying to discern whether there was a very slight difference, which would have been somewhat accentuated had he dropped the weights from a greater height. His report is, therefore, not quite so accurate as the one Philoponus gave at the end of the sixth century.

Galileo, who had performed this particular experiment with greater care than Stevin, reported it in final form:

"But I, Simplicio, who have made the test can assure you that a cannon ball weighing one or two hundred pounds, or even more, will not reach the ground by as much as a span ahead of a musket ball weighing only half a pound, provided both are dropped from a height of 200 cubits . . . the larger outstrips the smaller by two finger-breadths, that is, when the larger has reached the ground, the other is short of it by two finger-breadths."

The Need for a New Physics

What, you may still wonder, has the relative speed of light and heavy falling objects to do with either a world system in which the earth is in motion or the earlier systems in which the earth was at rest? The answer lies in the fact that the old system of physics associated with the name of Aristotle was a complete system of physics developed for a universe at the center of which the earth was at rest; hence, to overthrow that system by putting the earth in motion required a new physics. Clearly, if it could be shown that the old physics was inadequate, or even that it led to wrong conclusions, one would have a very powerful argument for rejecting the old system of the universe. Conversely, to make people accept a new system, it would be necessary to provide a new physics for it.

I assume, of course, that you, the reader of this book, accept the "modern" point of view, which holds that the sun is at rest and that the planets move around it. For the moment let us not inquire what we mean by the statement "The sun is at rest," or how we might prove it, but simply concentrate on the fact that the earth is in motion. How fast does it move? The earth rotates upon its axis once in every 24 hours. At the equator the circumference of the earth is approximately 24,000 miles, and so the speed of rotation of any observer at the earth's equator

is 1000 miles per hour. This is a linear speed of about
1500 feet per second. Conceive the following experiment. A rock is thrown straight up into the air. The time
in which it rises is, let us say, two seconds, while a similar
time is required for its descent. During four seconds the
rotation of the earth will have moved the point from
which the object was thrown a distance of some 6000
feet, a little over a mile. But the rock does not strike the
earth one mile away; it lands very near the point from
which it was thrown. We ask, How can this be possible?
How can the earth be twirling around at this tremendous
speed of 1000 miles per hour and yet we do not hear the
wind whistling as the earth leaves the air behind it? Or,
to take one of the other classical objections to the idea
of a moving earth, consider a bird perched on the limb
of a tree. The bird sees a worm on the ground and lets
go of the tree. In the meanwhile the earth goes whirling
by at this enormous rate, and the bird, though flapping
its wings as hard as it can, will never achieve sufficient
speed to find the worm—unless the worm is located to
the west. But it is a fact of observation that birds do fly
from trees to the earth and eat worms that lie to the east
as well as to the west. Unless you can see your way
clearly through these problems without a moment's
thought, you do not really live modern physics to its
fullest, and for you the statement that the earth rotates
upon its axis once in 24 hours really has no meaning.

If the daily rotation presents a serious problem, think
of the annual motion of the earth in its orbit. Let us compute the speed with which the earth moves in its orbit
around the sun. There are 60 seconds in a minute and
60 minutes in an hour, or 3600 seconds in an hour. Multiply this number by 24 to get 86,400 seconds in a day.
Multiply this by 365¼ days, and the result is a little more
than 30 million seconds in a year. To find the speed at
which the earth moves around the sun, we have to compute the size of the earth's orbit and divide it by the time

it takes the earth to move through the orbit. This path is roughly a circle with a radius of about 93 million miles, and a circumference of about 580,000,000 miles (the circumference of the circle is equal to the radius multiplied by 2π). This is equivalent to saying that the earth moves through about 3,000,000,000,000 feet in every year. The speed of the earth is thus

$$\frac{3,000,000,000,000 \text{ feet}}{30,000,000 \text{ seconds}} = 100,000 \text{ ft/sec}$$

Each of the questions raised about the rotating earth can be raised again in magnified form with regard to an earth moving in an orbit. This speed of 100,000 feet per second, or about 19 miles per second, shows us the great difficulty encountered at the beginning of the chapter. Let us ask this question: Is it possible for us to move at a speed of 19 miles per second and not be aware of it? Suppose we dropped an object from a height of 16 feet; it would take about one second to strike the ground. According to our calculation, while this object was falling the earth should have been rushing away underneath, and the object would strike the ground some 19 miles from the point where it was dropped! And as for the birds on the trees, if a bird hanging on a limb for dear life were to let go for an instant, it would be lost out in space forever. Yet the fact is that birds are not lost in space but continue to inhabit the earth and to fly about it singing gaily.

These examples show us how difficult it really is to face the consequences of an earth in motion. It is plain that our ordinary ideas are inadequate to explain the observed facts of daily experience on an earth that is either rotating or moving in its orbit. There should be no doubt, therefore, that the shift from the concept of a stationary earth to a moving earth necessarily involved the birth of a new physics.

CHAPTER 2

The Old Physics

The old physics is sometimes known as the physics of common sense, because it is the kind of physics that most people believe and act upon intuitively, or the kind of physics that seems to appeal to anyone who uses his native intelligence but has had no training in the modern principles of dynamics. Above all, it is a kind of physics that is particularly well adapted to the concepts of an earth at rest. Sometimes this is known as Aristotelian physics, because the major exposition of it in antiquity came from the philosopher-scientist Aristotle, who lived in Greece in the fourth century B.C. Aristotle was a pupil of Plato, and was himself tutor of Alexander the Great, who, like Aristotle, came from Macedonia.

Aristotle's Physics of Common Sense

Aristotle was an important figure in the development of thought, and not for his contributions to science alone. His writings on politics and economics are masterpieces, and his works on ethics and metaphysics still challenge philosophers. Aristotle is looked upon as the founder of biology, and Charles Darwin paid him this homage a hundred years ago: "Cuvier and Linnaeus have both been in many ways my two gods, but neither of them could hold a candle to old Aristotle." It was

Aristotle who first introduced the concept of classification of animals, and he also brought to a high point the method of controlled observation in the biological sciences. One subject he studied was the embryology of the chick; it was his ambition to discover the sequence of development of the organs. Methodically he opened chicks' eggs on successive days, and made careful comparisons to find out the stages whereby the chick develops from an unformed embryo to a perfectly formed young chicken. Aristotle also was the first to formalize the process of deductive reasoning, in the form of the syllogism:

> All men are mortal.
> Socrates is a man.
> Therefore, Socrates is mortal.

Aristotle pointed out that what makes such a set of three statements a valid progression is not the particular content of "man," "Socrates," and "mortal," but rather the form. For another example: all minerals are heavy, iron is a mineral, therefore iron is heavy. This is one of many valid forms of syllogism that were described by Aristotle in his great treatise on logic and reasoning, comprising both deduction and induction.

Aristotle stressed the importance of observation in sciences other than biology, notably astronomy. For instance, among the many arguments he advanced to prove that the earth is more or less a sphere was the shape of the shadow cast by the earth on the moon, as observed during an eclipse. If the earth is a sphere, then the shadow cast by the earth is a cone; thus when the moon enters the earth's shadow, the shape of the shadow will be roughly circular. It may be observed that an eclipse of the moon occurs only when the moon is full and that the shadow boundary is not exactly a circle. The explanation is that the edge of the shadow of the earth is the intersection of a sphere and a cone, which does not appear to us as a perfect circle. But if the earth were a flat disc, rather than a roughly spherical body, then the shadow would not always have the shape of approximately a circle. Or again, read Aristotle's description of the moon rainbow:

"The rainbow is seen by day, and it was formerly thought that it never appeared by night as a moon rainbow. This opinion was due to the rarity of the occurrence; it was not observed, for, though it does happen, it does so rarely. The reason is that the colors are not easy to see in the dark and that many other conditions must coincide, and all that in a single day in the month. For if there is to be a moon rainbow it must be at full moon, and then as the moon is either rising or setting. So we have met with only two instances of a moon rainbow in more than fifty years."

These examples are sufficient to show that Aristotle cannot be described as purely an "armchair philosopher." It is true, nevertheless, that Aristotle did not put every statement to the test of experiment. He undoubtedly believed what he had been told by his teachers, just as successive generations believed what Aristotle had said. Often this is taken to be a basis for criticizing both Aristotle and his successors as scientists. But it should be kept in mind that no student ever verifies all the statements he reads, or even most of them, especially those he finds in textbooks or handbooks. Life is too short.

The "Natural" Motion of Objects

Now let us examine Aristotle's statements about motion. Basic to Aristotle's discussion was the principle that all the objects we encounter on this earth are made up of "four elements," air, earth, fire, and water. These are the "elements" we talk about in ordinary conversation when we say that someone out in a storm has "braved the elements." We mean that such a person has been in a windstorm, a dust storm, a rainstorm, and so on, not that he has struggled through a tornado of pure hydrogen, or fluorine. Aristotle observed that some objects on earth appear to be light and others appear to be heavy. He attributed the property of being heavy or light to the proportion in each body of the different elements—earth being "naturally" heavy and fire being "naturally" light, water and air being intermediate between those two extremes. What, he asked, was the "natural" motion of such an object? He replied that if it was heavy, its natural motion would be downward, whereas if it was light its natural motion would be upward. Smoke, being light, ascends straight upward unless blown by the wind, while a rock, an apple, or a piece of iron falls straight downward when dropped. Hence, for Aristotle the "natural" (or unimpeded) motion of a terrestrial object is straight upward or straight downward, upward and downward being reckoned along a straight line from the center of the earth through the observer.

Aristotle was, of course, aware that very often objects move in ways other than those just described. For instance, an arrow shot from a bow starts its flight apparently in a straight line that is more or less perpendicular to a line from the center of the earth to the observer. A ball at the end of a string can be whirled around in a circle. A rock can be thrown straight upward. Such motion, according to Aristotle, is "violent" or contrary to the nature of the body. Such motion occurs only when some force is acting to start and to keep the body moving contrary to its nature. A rock with a string tied around it can be lifted upward, and so made to undergo violent motion, but the moment the string is broken the rock will begin to fall downward in a natural motion, seeking its natural place.

Let us now consider the motion of heavenly objects,

the stars, planets, and the sun itself. These bodies appear
to move around the earth in circles, the sun, moon,
planets, and stars rising in the east, traveling through the
heavens, and setting in the west (except for those cir-
cumpolar stars which move in small circles but never get
below the horizon). According to Aristotle, the celestial
bodies are not made of the same four elements as the
earthly bodies. They are made of a "fifth element" or
"aether." The natural motion of a body composed of
aether is circular, so that the observed circular motion
of the heavenly bodies is their natural motion, according
to their nature, just as motion upward or downward in a
straight line is the natural motion for a terrestrial object.

The "Incorruptible" Heavens

In the Aristotelian philosophy the heavenly bodies
have one or two other properties of interest. The aether
of which they are made is a material which is unchangeable, or to use the old phrase "incorruptible." This is in
contrast to the four elements we find on earth—they are
subject to change, or "corruptible." Thus on the earth
we find both "coming into being" and "decay" and
"passing away," things being born and dying. But in the
heavens nothing ever changes; all remain the same: the
same stars, the same eternal planets, the same sun, the
same moon. The planets, the stars, and the sun were considered to be "perfect" and throughout the centuries
were often compared to eternal diamonds or precious
stones because of their unchanging qualities. The only
heavenly object in which any kind of change or "imper-
fection" could be detected was the moon—but the moon,
after all, was the heavenly body nearest the earth, and
was a kind of dividing point between the terrestrial region of change (or corruptibility) and the celestial region of permanence and incorruptibility.

It should be observed that in this system all the heavenly objects circling the earth are more or less alike, and are all different from the earth—in physical characteristics, composition, and "essential properties." Thus one might understand why the earth remains still and does not move, whereas all the heavenly objects do move. Furthermore, the earth not only had no "local motion," or movement from one place to another, but it was not even supposed to rotate upon its axis. The chief physical reason for this, according to the old system, was that it was not "natural" for the earth to have a circular motion; it would be contrary to its nature, whether the motion be in orbit around the sun or a daily rotation upon its own axis.

The Factors of Motion

Let us now examine a little more closely the Aristotelian physics of motion for terrestrial bodies. In all motion, said Aristotle, there are two major factors: the motive force, which we shall denote here by F and the resistance which we shall denote by R. For motion to occur, according to Aristotle, it is necessary that the motive force be greater than the resistance. Therefore our first principle of motion is

$$F > R \qquad (1)$$

or, force must be greater than resistance. Let us now explore the effects of different resistances, all the while keeping the motive force constant. Our experiment will be performed with falling bodies, each of which will be allowed to fall freely, starting from rest, through a different resistant medium. In order to keep the conditions constant, we shall have the falling bodies all be spheres, so that the effect of their shape on their motion will be the same. Aristotle was, of course, quite aware that the speed of an object, all other things being equal, generally depends upon its shape, a fact we already have demonstrated with our parachute.

Now to our experiment. Two identical steel balls with the same size, shape, and weight are used. We shall allow the two to fall simultaneously, one through air, the other through water. To do this experiment, you need a long cylinder filled with water; hold the two balls side by side, one over the water and the other at the same height but just outside this column of water (Fig. 1). When you

Fig. 1.

release them simultaneously, you will see that there is no question that the speed of the one moving through air is very much greater than that of the one falling through the water. To prove that the results of the experiment did not derive from the fact that the balls were made of steel or had a particular weight, the experiment can be repeated using smaller steel balls, a pair of glass balls or brass balls, and so on. On a smaller scale, anyone can repeat this experiment by using two glass "marbles" and a highball glass filled to the brim with water. The result of this experiment can be written in the form of an equation, in which we express the fact that, all other things being equal, the speed in water (which resists or impedes the motion) is less than the speed in air (which does not impede the motion as much as water does):

$$V \propto \frac{1}{R}$$

$$(2)$$

or the speed is inversely proportional to the resistance of the medium through which the body moves. It is a common experience that water resists motion; anyone who has tried to run through the water at the edge of the beach knows how much the water resists his motion in comparison to the air.

The experiment is now to be performed with two cylinders, one filled with water and the other filled with oil (Fig. 2). The oil resists the motion even more than

Fig. 2.

the water; when the two identical steel spheres are dropped simultaneously, the one in water reaches the bottom long before the one falling through oil. Because the resistance R_o of oil is greater than the resistance R_w of water, we can now predict that if any pair of identical objects is let fall through these liquids, the one falling through water will drop through a given height faster than the one falling through oil. This prediction can easily be verified. Next, since it has been found that the resistance R_w of water is greater than the resistance R_a of air,

$$R_o > R_w$$
$$R_w > R_a$$

$$(3)$$

the resistance of oil must necessarily be greater than that of air,

$$R_0 > R_a \qquad (4)$$

This, too, can be verified by repeating the initial experiment with a cylinder filled with air rather than water.

Let us next observe the effects of different motive forces. In this experiment we again use the long cylinder filled with water. In it we drop a small and a large steel ball simultaneously. We find that the large steel ball, the heavier of the two, reaches the bottom before the lighter one. Here, it might be argued, the size could have some effect, but if anything the larger ball should meet a greater resistance than the smaller one. Nevertheless, the result is valid. Evidently the greater the force to overcome a particular resistance, the greater the speed. This experiment may be repeated, this time using one ball of steel and the other of glass, so that the two will be exactly the same size but of different weights. Once again, it is found that the heavier ball seems to be much better able to overcome the resistance of the medium; thus it reaches the bottom first or attains the greater speed. The experiment can also be done in oil, and in various other liquids—alcohol, milk, and so on—to produce the same general result. In equation form, we can state the conclusions of this experiment as follows:

$$V \propto F \qquad (5)$$

or, all other things being equal, the greater the force the greater the speed.

We may now combine Equation (2) and Equation (5) into a single equation as follows:

$$V \propto \frac{F}{R} \qquad (6)$$

or, the speed is proportional to the motive force and inversely proportional to the resistance of the medium: Or, the speed is proportional to the force divided by the resistance. This equation is often known as the Aristotelian law of motion. It should be pointed out that Aristotle himself did not write his results in the form of equations, a modern way of expressing such relationships. Aristotle and most early scientists, including Galileo, preferred to compare speeds to speeds, forces to forces, and resistances to resistances. Thus instead of writing Equation (5) as we have done, they would have preferred the statement

$$V_g : V_s :: F_g : F_s$$

The ratio of speeds of the glass and steel balls is compared with the ratio of the forces with which these balls are moved downward. This is equivalent to the general statement that the speed of the glass ball is to the speed of the steel ball as the motive force of the glass ball is to the motive force of the steel ball.

Let us now study Equation (6), in order to discover some of its limitations. It is clear that this equation cannot be applied generally, because if the motive force should equal the resistance, the equation would not give the result that the speed V is equal to zero; nor does it give us a zero result when the force F is less than the resistance R. Hence Equation (6) is subject to the arbitrary limitation imposed by Equation (1), and is only true when the force is greater than the resistance. But this is to say that the equation is not a universal statement of the conditions of motion.

It is sometimes held that this equation may have arisen from the study of an unequal arm balance, say with equal weights on the two arms, or perhaps an equal arm balance with unequal weights at the ends of the two arms. In this case it is impossible for F to be less than R, because the greater weight is always the motive force, while the lesser weight is always the resistance. Furthermore, in the equal arm balance if $F = R$ there will be no motion.

There are two final aspects of the law of motion, which we must introduce before we leave the subject. The first is that the law itself does not tell us anything about the stages by which an object falling from rest acquires the speed V. The law only tells us something about the speed itself: obviously some kind of "average" speed or "final" speed, since its measure is simply the time rate of traversing a given distance

$$V \propto \frac{D}{T} \tag{7}$$

which holds for average speed or for motion at a constant speed, but not for accelerated or constantly changing speeds. Was it not known to Aristotle that the speed of a falling body starts from zero and by gradual stages attains its final value?

Motion of Bodies Falling through Air

Perhaps of greater significance to us than any of the preceding arguments is the outcome of another experiment. Thus far we have given the kind of positive experience that would make us have confidence in Aristotle's law of motion, but we have omitted one very crucial experiment. Let us return to a consideration of two objects of the same size, the same shape, but of different weight, or of different motive force F. We said that if these were dropped simultaneously through water, or through oil, it would be observed that the heavier one would descend more quickly. (The reader—before going on with the rest of this chapter and the rest of this book —will find it interesting to stop and perform these experiments for himself.) Now we come to the last in that earlier sequence of experiments; it consists of dropping two objects of the same size but of unequal weight in the same medium, but having the medium be *air*. Let us assume that the weight of one of our objects is exactly twice the weight of the other, which might imply in the old view that the speed of the heavier object should be just twice that of the lighter one. For a constant distance of fall, the speed is inversely proportional to the time, so that

$$V \propto \frac{1}{T} \tag{8}$$

or

$$\frac{V_1}{V_2} = \frac{T_2}{T_1} \tag{9}$$

or, the speeds are inversely proportional to the times of descent. Hence, the time of descent of the heavier ball should be just half the time of descent of the lighter one. To perform the experiment, stand on a chair and drop the two objects together so that they will strike the bare floor. One good way of dropping them more or less simultaneously is to hold them horizontally between the first and second fingers of one hand. Then suddenly open the two fingers, and the two balls will begin to fall together. What is the result of this experiment?

Instead of describing the results of this experiment, let me suggest that you do it for yourself. Then compare your result with those obtained by John the Grammarian and also with the description given in the sixteenth century by Stevin, and finally with that given by Galileo in his famous book *Two New Sciences* a little more than 300 years ago.

One question you should ask yourself at this point is this: Evidently Equation (6) does not hold for air, but did it really hold for the other media which we explored? In order to see whether or not Equation (6) is an accurate quantitative statement, ask yourself whether it was merely a definition of "resistance," or if there is some other means of measuring "resistance," how were the speeds measured. Is it enough, in order to measure speed, to use Equation (8), and to measure the time of fall?

In any event, most of you, I think, will have found that with the exception of the experiment of two unequal objects falling through air, the Aristotelian system sounds reasonable enough to be believed. There is no cause for us to condemn unduly either Aristotle or any Aristotelian physicist who had never performed the experiment of simultaneously dropping two objects of unequal weight in air.

The Impossibility of a Moving Earth

But what, you may still ask, has any of this to do with the earth's being at rest rather than in motion? For the answer let us turn to Aristotle's book *On the Heavens*. Here one finds the statement that some have considered the earth to be at rest, while others have said the earth moves. But there are many reasons why the earth cannot move. In order to have a rotation about an axis, each part of the earth would have to move in a circle, says Aristotle; but the study of the actual behavior of its parts shows that the natural earthly motion is along a straight line toward the center. "The motion, therefore, being enforced, [violent] and unnatural, could not be eternal; but the order of the world is eternal." The natural motion of all bits of earthly matter is toward the center of the universe, which happens to coincide with the center of the earth. In "evidence" that earthly bodies do in fact move toward the center of the earth, Aristotle says, "We see that weights moving toward the earth do not move in parallel lines," but apparently at some angle to one another. "To our previous reasons," he then points out, "we may add that heavy objects, if thrown forcibly upwards in a straight line, come back to their starting place, even if the force hurls them to an unlimited distance." Thus, if a body were thrown straight up, and then fell straight down, these directions being reckoned with respect to the center of the universe, it would not land on earth exactly at the spot from which it was thrown, if the earth moved away during the interval. This is a direct consequence of the "natural" quality of straight-line motion for earthly objects.

The preceding arguments show how the Aristotelian principles of natural and violent (unnatural) motion may be applied to prove the impossibility of terrestrial movement. But what of the Aristotelian "law of motion," given in Equation (6) or Equation (9)? How is this specifically related to the earth's being at rest? The answer is given clearly in the beginning of Ptolemy's *Almagest,* the standard ancient work on geocentric astronomy. Ptolemy wrote, following Aristotelian principles, that if the earth had a motion "it would, as it was carried down, have got ahead of every other falling body, in virtue of its enormous excess of size, and the animals and all separate weights would have been left behind floating on the air, while the earth, for its part, at its great speed, would have fallen out of the universe itself." This follows plainly from the notion that bodies fall with speeds proportional to their respective weights. And many a scientist must have agreed with Ptolemy's final comment, "But indeed this sort of suggestion has only to be thought of in order to be seen to be utterly ridiculous."

CHAPTER 3

The Earth and the Universe

Very often the year 1543 is taken to be the natal year of modern science. In that year there were published two major books which led to significant changes in man's concept of nature and the world: one was the Polish churchman Nicholas Copernicus's *On the Revolutions of the Celestial Spheres* and the other the Fleming Andreas Vesalius's *On the Fabric of the Human Body*. The latter dealt with man from the point of view of exact anatomical observation, and so reintroduced into physiology and medicine the spirit of experiment that had characterized the writings of the Greek anatomists and physiologists, of whom the last and the greatest had been Galen. Copernicus's book introduced a new system of astronomy, which ran counter to the generally accepted notions that the earth is at rest. It will be our purpose here to discuss only certain selected features of the Copernican system, notably some consequences of considering the earth to be in motion. We shall not consider in any detail the relative advantages and disadvantages of the system as a whole, nor even compare its merits step by step with those of the older system. Our primary consideration is to explore what consequences the concept of a moving earth had for the development of a new science —dynamics.

Copernicus and the Birth of Modern Science

Even in ancient Greece it was suggested that the earth may have a daily rotation on its axis and make an annual revolution in a huge orbit around the sun. Proposed by Aristarchus in the third century B.C., this system of the universe lost out to one in which the earth was at rest. Even when, almost 2000 years later, Copernicus published his account of a system of the universe based on these two terrestrial motions, there was no general assent. Eventually, of course, Copernicus's book proved to have been the seed of the whole scientific revolution that culminated in Isaac Newton's magnificent foundation of modern physics. Looking backwards, we can see how the acceptance of the Copernican concept of a moving earth necessarily implied a non-Aristotelian physics. Why, then, was none of this sequence apparent to the contemporaries of Copernicus? And why did not Copernicus himself produce that scientific revolution which has altered the world to such an extent that we still are not fully aware of all its consequences? In this chapter we shall explore these questions, and in particular we shall see why Copernicus's proposal of a system of the world in which the earth was held to be in motion and the sun to be at rest was not of itself sufficient for a rejection of the old physics.

At the outset we must make it plain that Copernicus (1473–1543) was in many ways more of a conservative than a revolutionary. Many of the ideas he introduced had already existed in the literature, and again and again the fact that he was unable to go beyond the basic principles of Aristotelian physics hampered him. When we talk today about the "Copernican system," we usually mean a system of the universe quite different from that described in Copernicus's *De revolutionibus orbium caelestium,* to give the original Latin title of the book.

The reason for this procedure is that we wish to honor Copernicus for his innovations, and do so at the expense of accuracy by referring to the sun-centered system as "Copernican."

The System of Concentric Spheres

But before describing the Copernican system, let me state some of the basic features of the two principal pre-Copernican systems. One, attributed to Eudoxus, was improved by another Greek astronomer, Callippus, and received its finishing touches from Aristotle. This is the system known as the "concentric spheres." In this system each planet, the sun and moon, were considered to be fixed on the equators of separate spheres, which rotated upon their axes, the earth being stationary at the center. While each sphere was rotating, the ends of the axis of rotation were fixed in another sphere, which was also rotating—with a different period and about an axis that did not have the same orientation as the axis of the inner sphere.

For some planets there could be as many as four spheres, each embedded in the next, with the result that there would be a variety of motions. For instance, one of these spheres could account for the fact that wherever the planet happened to be among the stars it would be made to revolve once around the earth in every 24 hours. There would be another such sphere to move the sun in its daily apparent revolution, another for the moon, and another for the fixed stars. The set of inner spheres for each planet would account for the fact that a planet does not appear to move through the heavens with only a daily motion, but also shifts its position from day to day with respect to the fixed stars. Thus a planet will sometimes be seen in one constellation, and again in another. Because planets are seen to wander among the fixed stars from night to night, they derive the name "planet" from the Greek verb meaning "to wander." One of the observed features of this wandering is that its direction is not constant. The usual direction of motion is to progress slowly eastward, but every now and again the planet stops its eastward motion (reaching a stationary point) and then (Fig. 3) moves for a short while westward,

Fig. 3.

until it reaches another stationary point, after which it resumes its original eastward motion through the heavens. The eastward motion is known as "direct" motion, the westward motion as "retrograde." By the proper combination of spheres Eudoxus was able to construct a model to show how combinations of circular motion could produce the observed direct and retrograde apparent motion of the planets. It is the same set of "spheres" that appears in the title of Copernicus's book.

After the decline of Greece, science fell into the hands of the Islamic or Arabian astronomers. Some among them elaborated on Eudoxus and Aristotle and introduced many further spheres in order to make the predictions of this system agree more exactly with observation.

These spheres, obtaining a certain reality, were thought to be made of crystal; the system acquired the title of "crystalline spheres." Because it was held that the orientation of the stars and planets had an important infleunce on the affairs of men, it came to be believed that the influence of the planet emanated not from the object itself but from the sphere to which it was attached. In this belief we may see the origin of the expression "sphere of influence," still used today in a political and economic sense.

Ptolemy and the System of Epicycles and Deferents

The other major rival system of antiquity was elaborated by Claudius Ptolemy, one of the greatest astronomers of the ancient world, and was based in some measure on concepts that had been introduced by the geometer Apollonius of Perga and the astronomer Hipparchus. The final product, known generally as the Ptolemaic system, in contrast to the Eudoxus-Aristotle system of homocentric (common-centered) spheres, had enormous flexibility, and as a consequence enormous complexity. The basic devices were used in various combinations. First of all, consider a point P moving uniformly in a circle around the point E, as in Fig. 4A. Here

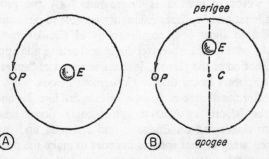

Fig. 4.

is an illustration of uniform circular motion that permits neither stationary points nor retrogradation. Nor does it account for the fact that the planets do not have a constant speed as they appear to move around the earth. At most such a motion could be observed only in the behavior of the fixed stars, for Hipparchus had seen even the sun moving with variable velocity, an observation connected with the fact that the seasons are not of the same length. In Fig. 4B., the earth is not at the exact center C of that circle, but is off-center, at the point E. Then it is clear that if the point P corresponds to a planet (or to the sun), it will not appear to move uniformly with respect to the fixed stars as seen from the earth, even though its motion along the circle is in fact uniform.

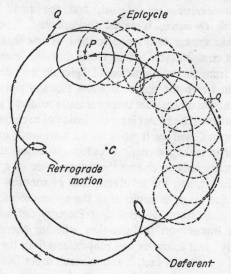

Fig. 5. Ptolemy's device to account for the wanderings of the planets assumed a complicated combination of motions. The planet Q traveled around P in a circle (dotted lines) while P moved in a circle around C. The solid line with loops is the path Q would follow in the combined motion.

If the earth and heavenly body form such an eccentric system, rather than a homocentric system, there will be times when the sun or planet will be very near the earth (perigee), and times when the sun or planet will be very far from the earth (apogee). Thus we should expect a variation in the brightness of the planets, which is also observed.

Next, we shall introduce one of Ptolemy's chief devices to account for the motion of the planets. Let us assume that while the point P moves uniformly on a circle about the center C (Fig. 5), a second point Q moves in a circle about the point P. The result will be to produce a curve with a series of loops or cusps. The large circle on which P moves is called the circle of reference, or the deferent, and the small circle on which Q moves is called the epicycle. Thus the Ptolemaic system is often described as one based on deferent and epicycle. It is clear that the curve resulting from the combination of epicycle and deferent is one in which the planet at some times is nearer the center than at others, that there are also stationary points, and that when the planet is on the inside of each loop, an observer at C will see it move with a retrograde motion. In order to make the motion conform to observation, it is necessary only to choose the relative size of epicycle and deferent, and the relative speeds of rotation of the two circles, so as to conform to the appearances.

It is plain from his book that Ptolemy did not ever commit himself on the question whether there were "actually" real epicycles and real deferents in the heavens. As a matter of fact, it seems much more likely that for him the system that he described was a "model" of the universe, and not necessarily the "true" picture—whatever those words may mean. That is, it was the Greek ideal, reaching its highest point in the writings of Ptolemy, to construct a model that would enable the astronomer to predict the observations, or—to use the

*Fig. 6. With epicycle and deferent (and ingenuity) as-
tronomers could describe almost any observed planetary motion and still stay within the bounds of the
Ptolemaic system. In (A) point P moves on circle with
center C, which moves on smaller circle centered at X.
In (B) the effect of the combination of deferent and
epicycle is to shift the apparent center of P's orbit from
C to C'. In (C) the combination yields an elliptical
curve. The figure in (D) traces the path of P moving
along an epicycle on an epicycle; the center of P's
circle is R, which moves on a circle whose center, Q,
is on a circle centered at C.*

Greek expression—"to save appearances." Although often disparaged, this approach to science is very similar to that of the twentieth-century physicist, whose ambition is likewise to produce a model that will yield equations predicting the results of experiment—and often he must be satisfied with equations in the absence of a "model" in the ordinary workable sense.

Certain other features of the old Ptolemaic system may be listed briefly. The earth need not be at the center of the deferent circle, or, expressed differently, the deferent circle (Fig. 6A) could be eccentric rather than homocentric—that is, with a center different from the center of the earth. Furthermore, while the point P is moving about the big circle (Fig. 6B) of reference or deferent, its center C could be moving about a small circle, a combination which need not produce retrogradation, but which could have the effect of lifting the circle or transposing it or producing elliptical motion (Fig. 6C). Finally, there was a device known as the "equant" (Fig. 7). This was a point not at the center of a circle about which motion could be "uniformized." That is, consider a point P moving on a circle with center at C in relation to an equant. The point P moves in such a way that a line from P to the equant sweeps out equal angles in equal times; this has the effect that P does not move uniformly along its circular path for an observer elsewhere than at the equant. These devices could be used in many different combinations. The result was a system of much complexity. Many a man of learning could not believe that a system of forty or more "wheels within wheels" could possibly be turning about in the heavens, that the world was so complicated. It is said that Alfonso X, King of León and Castile, called Alfonso the Wise, who sponsored a famous set of astronomical tables in the thirteenth century, could not believe the system of the universe to be that intricate. When first taught the Ptolemaic system, he commented, according to legend: "If the Lord Almighty had consulted me before embarking upon the creation, I should have recommended something simpler."

Nowhere have the difficulties of understanding the Ptolemaic system been expressed so clearly as by the poet John Milton in his famous poem *Paradise Lost*.

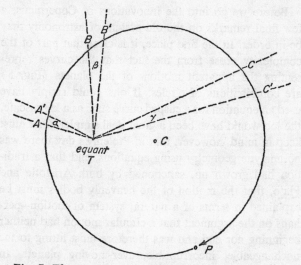

Fig. 7. The equant was a Ptolemaic device to explain apparent changes in a planet's speed. While the movement of P from A to A', from B to B', and from C to C' would not be uniform with respect to the center of the circle, C, it would be with respect to another point, T, the equant because the angles α, β, γ are equal. The planet moves along each of the arcs AA', BB' and CC' in the same time but, obviously, at different speeds.

Milton had been a schoolteacher, had actually taught the Ptolemaic system, and knew, therefore, whereof he wrote. In these lines the angel Raphael is replying to Adam's questions about the construction of the universe and telling him that God must surely be moved to laughter by men's activities:

> . . . when they come to model Heav'n
> And calculate the Stars, how they will wield
> The mighty frame, how build, unbuild, contrive
> To save appearances, how gird the Sphere
> With Centric and Eccentric scribbled o'er,
> Cycle and Epicycle, Orb in Orb . . .

Before we go into the innovations of Copernicus, a few final remarks on the old system of astronomy may be in order. In the first place, it is clear that part of the complexity arose from the fact that the curves representing the apparent motions of the planets (Fig. 5) are combinations of circles. If one could simply have used an equation for a cusped curve such as a lemniscate, the job would have been a great deal simpler. One must keep in mind, however, that in Ptolemy's day there was no analytic geometry using equations, and that a tradition had grown up, sanctioned by both Aristotle and Plato, that the motion of the heavenly bodies must be explained in terms of a natural system of motion—perhaps on the argument that a circular motion had neither beginning nor end and was therefore most fitting to the unchangeable, incorruptible, ever-moving planets. In any event, as we shall see, the idea of explaining planetary motion solely by combinations of circles remained in astronomy for a long, long time.

Apart from the fact that the Ptolemaic system worked, or could be made to work, the fact that it fitted in perfectly with the system of Aristotelian physics also is pertinent. The stars, planets, sun, and moon moved in circles or in combinations of circles, their "natural motion," while the earth did not partake of motion, being in its "natural place" at the center of the universe, and at rest. In the Ptolemaic system, then, there was no need to seek a new system of physics other than the one which accorded equally well with the system of homocentric spheres. Sometimes these two systems are described as being "geostatic," because in both of them the earth is at rest; the more customary expression is "geocentric," because in both of the two systems the earth is at the center of the universe.

Sun   Mercury   Venus · Earth   Moon   Mars

Jupiter   Saturn   Uranus   Neptune   Pluto

Fig. 8. The origins of the oldest planetary symbols are lost in antiquity, but the commonly accepted derivations stem from Latin and Greek mythology. The sun symbol probably represented a buckler (shield) with boss. The symbol for Mercury represented either his caduceus, the staff he carried, or his head and winged cap. The symbol of Venus was the looking glass associated with the goddess of love and beauty. The symbol for Mars, god of war, has been taken to represent either a warrior's head and helmet with nodding plume or a spear and shield. The symbol for Jupiter also has alternate derivations—either a crude hieroglyph of the eagle, "bird of Jove," or the first letter of Zeus, the Greek name of Jupiter. Saturn's symbol is an ancient scythe, emblem of the god of time. The symbol for Uranus is the first letter of its discoverer's name, Sir William Herschel (1738–1822), with the planet suspended from the crossbar. The trident was always carried by Neptune, god of the sea. The symbol for Pluto is an obvious monogram. It is interesting that the alchemists used the Mercury symbol for the metal mercury and the Venus symbol for copper. Today geneticists designate female with the Venus symbol and male with the Mars symbol.

Copernican Innovations

As Copernicus described his own system, it bore many resemblances to the system of Ptolemy. Copernicus admired Ptolemy enormously; in organizing his book, ordering the different chapters and choosing the sequence in which various topics were introduced, he followed Ptolemy's *Almagest.*

The transfer from a geostatic to a heliostatic (immobile sun) system did involve certain new explanations (Fig. 8A). To see them, let us begin as Copernicus did by considering the simplest form of the heliostatic uni-

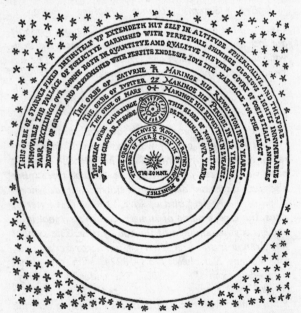

Fig. 8A. This diagram of the Copernican system is taken from Thomas Digges's A Perfit Description of the Caelestial Orbes *(1576), giving an English translation of a portion of Copernicus's* De revolutionibus. *Digges has added one feature to the system in making the sphere of the fixed stars infinite.*

verse. The sun is at the center, fixed and immobile, and around it there move in circles in the following order: Mercury, Venus, the earth with its moon, Mars, Jupiter, Saturn (Fig. 8A). Copernicus explained the daily apparent motions of the sun, moon, stars, and planets on the ground that the earth rotates upon its axis once a day. The other major appearances derived, he said, from a second motion of the earth, which was an orbital revolution about the sun, just like the orbits of the other planets. Each planet has a different period of revolution, the period being greater the farther the planet is from the sun. Thus retrograde motion is easily explained. Consider Mars (Fig. 9), which moves more slowly around the sun than the earth. Seven positions of the earth and Mars are shown at a time when Mars is passing the earth and when Mars is in opposition (that is, when a line from the sun to Mars passes through the earth). It will be seen that a line drawn from the earth to Mars at each of these successive positions will move first forward, then backward, and then forward again. Thus Copernicus not only could explain "naturally" how retrograde motion occurs, but could also show why it is that retrogradation is observed in Mars only at opposition, corresponding to the planet's crossing the meridian at midnight. In opposition, the planet is on the opposite side of the earth from the sun. This is why it will reach its highest position in the heavens at midnight, or will cross the meridian at midnight. In similar fashion (Fig. 10) one could see that for an inferior planet (Mercury or Venus) retrogradation would occur only at inferior conjunction, corresponding to the planet's crossing the meridian at noon. (When Venus or Mercury lies along a straight line from the earth to the sun, the position is called conjunction. These planets are in the center of retrogradations at inferior conjunction, when they lie between the earth and the sun. Then, they cross the meridian together with the sun at noon.) These two facts make perfect sense in a

Fig. 9. In the Copernican system the apparent retrograde motion of planets has a simple explanation; it is a matter of relative speeds. Here the sighting lines show why a superior planet, one farther from the sun than the earth is, seems to reverse its direction. It is traveling around the sun more slowly than the earth is.

Fig. 10. Retrograde motion of an inferior planet, whose orbit lies between the earth and sun, also is readily explained with sighting lines. Venus travels around the sun faster than the earth does.

heliocentric or heliostatic system, but if the *earth* were the center of motion, as in the Ptolemaic system, why should the retrogradation of the planets depend on their orientation with respect to the *sun*?

Still sticking to the simplified model of circular orbits, let us observe next that Copernicus was able to determine the scale of the solar system. Consider Venus (Fig. 11). Venus is seen only as evening star or morning star,

Fig. 11

because it is either a little ahead of the sun or a little behind the sun but never 180 degrees away from the sun, as a superior planet may be. The Ptolemaic system (Fig. 11A) accounted for this only by the arbitrary assumption that the centers of the epicycles of Venus and Mercury were permanently fixed on a line from the earth to the sun; that is to say, the deferents of Mercury and Venus, just like the sun, moved around the earth once in every year. In the Copernican system one had merely to assume that the orbits of Venus and Mercury (Fig. 11B) were within the orbit of the earth.

In the Copernican system, furthermore, one could compute the distance from Venus to the sun. Observations made night after night would indicate when Venus could be seen at its farthest elongation (angular separation) from the sun. When this event occurred, the angu-

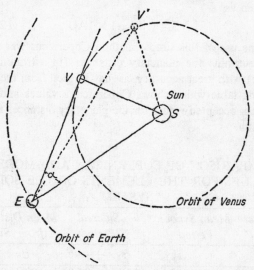

Fig. 12. Computing the distance from Venus to the sun became possible in the Copernican system. When the angular separation (that is, the angle α of Venus from the sun) is at the maximum, the line of sight from the earth to Venus (EV) is tangent to Venus's orbit and therefore perpendicular to the radius VS. Computing the length of VS is an easy problem in elementary trigonometry. At any other orientation, say V', the angular separation is not maximum.

lar separation could be determined. As may be seen in Fig. 12, the maximum elongation occurs when a line from the earth to Venus is tangent to Venus's orbit and thus perpendicular to a line from the sun to Venus. From simple trigonometry we can write this equation and from a table of tangents easily calculate the length ES.

$$\frac{VS}{ES} = \text{sine } \alpha \qquad (1)$$

The distance ES, or the average size of the radius of the earth's orbit in the Copernican system, is known as an "astronomical unit." Thus Equation (1) may be rewritten as

$$VS = (\text{sine } \alpha) \times 1AU \qquad (2)$$

By the use of this simple method Copernicus was able to determine the planetary distances (in astronomical units) with great accuracy, as may be seen from the following table which shows Copernicus's values and the present accepted values for the planetary distances from the sun.

COMPARISON OF COPERNICAN AND MODERN VALUES FOR THE ELEMENTS OF THE SOLAR SYSTEM

Planet	Mean Synodic* Period		Sidereal Period		Mean Distance from Sun**	
	C	M	C	M	C	M
Mercury	116d	116d	88d	87.91d	0.36	0.391
Venus	584d	584d	225d	225.00d	0.72	0.721
Earth			365¼d	365.26d	1.0	1.000
Mars	780d	780d	687d	686.98d	1.5	1.52
Jupiter	399d	399d	12y	11.86y	5	5.2
Saturn	378d	378d	30y	29.51y	9	9.5

* Synodic periods are times between conjunctions of the same bodies.
** Expressed in astronomical units.

Furthermore, Copernicus was able to determine with equal accuracy the time required for each planet to complete a revolution of 360 degrees around the sun, or its sidereal period. Since Copernicus knew the relative sizes of the planetary orbits and the sidereal periods of the planets, he was able to predict to a tolerable degree of accuracy the planets' future positions. In the Ptolemaic system, the distances of the planets played no role whatsoever, since there was no way of determining them from observations. So long as the relative sizes and relative periods of motion on deferent and epicycle were the same, the observations or appearances would be identical, as may be seen in Fig. 13. That the Ptolemaic system dealt chiefly in angle rather than in distance may be seen

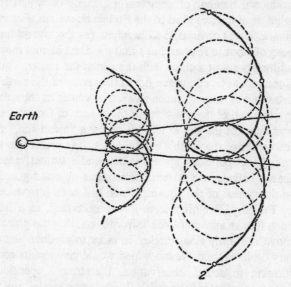

Earth

Fig. 13. In the Ptolemaic system predictions of planetary positions leaned on measurement of angles, not distances. This illustration shows that observations would be the same regardless of distance if the relative periods of motion were the same.

most clearly in the example of the moon. It was one of the major features of the Ptolemaic system that the moon's apparent position could be described with a relatively high degree of accuracy. But this required a special device, and had the moon really followed the contrived path it would have had an enormous variation in apparent size, far greater than is observed.

I have said earlier that the system of a single circle for each planet with a single circle for the moon, and two different motions for the earth, constituted a simplified version of the Copernican system. The fact of the matter is that such a system does not agree with observation, except in a rough way. In order to make his system more accurate, therefore, Copernicus found it necessary to introduce a number of complexities, many of which remind us of devices used in the Ptolemaic system. For instance, it was obvious to Copernicus (as the inverse had been obvious to Hipparchus) that the earth cannot move uniformly about a circle with the sun at the center. Thus Copernicus placed the sun not at the center of the earth's orbit, but at some distance away. The center of the solar system, and of the universe, in the system of Copernicus was thus not the sun at all, but rather a "mean sun," or the center of the earth's orbit. Hence, it is preferable to call the Copernican system a heliostatic system rather than a heliocentric system. Copernicus objected greatly to the system of the equant, which had been introduced by Ptolemy. For his system it was necessary, as it had been for the ancient Greek astronomers, that the planets move uniformly along circles. In order to produce planetary orbits around the sun which would give results conforming to actual observation, therefore, Copernicus ended up by introducing circles moving on circles, much as Ptolemy had done. The chief difference here is that Ptolemy had introduced such combinations of circles also to account for retrograde motion, while Copernicus (Fig. 14) accounted for retrograde motion, as we have seen, by the fact that the planets move in their successive orbits at different speeds.* A comparison of the two figures representing the Ptolemaic and Copernican systems does not show that one was in any obvious way "simpler" than the other.

Copernicus versus Ptolemy

What were the advantages and disadvantages in the Copernican system as compared to the Ptolemaic system? In the first place, one decided advantage of the Copernican system was the relative ease in explaining retrograde motion of planets and showing why their positions relative to the sun determined the retrograde motions. A second advantage of the Copernican system was that it afforded a basis for determining the distances of the planets from the sun and from the earth.

It is sometimes said that the Copernican system was a great simplification, but this is based upon a misunderstanding. If the Copernican system is considered in the rudimentary form of a single circle for each planet around the sun, then this assumption would be valid. But when we consider that Copernicus had to use circle upon circle just as Ptolemy did, then the only major simplification is that the circles needed for the daily apparent rotations of the sun, stars, planets, and moon in the Ptolemaic system could be eliminated by the assumption that the earth rotated daily upon its axis—but almost all the other circles would remain.

Now, what were the disadvantages of the Copernican

* A final complexity of the Copernican system arose from the difficulties Copernicus experienced in accounting for the fact that the axis of the rotating earth remains fixed in its orientation with respect to the stars even though the earth moves in its orbit. The "motion" introduced by Copernicus was found to be unnecessary. Galileo later showed that because no force is acting to turn the earth's axis, it does *not* move but always remains parallel to itself.

Fig. 14. The Ptolemaic system (A) and the Copernican system (B) were of about equal complexity, as can be

system? The first was the absence of any annual parallax of the fixed stars. The phenomenon of parallax refers to the shift in view that occurs when the same object is seen from two different positions. This is the principle upon which range finders for artillery and for photographic cameras are built. Consider the motion of the earth in the Copernican system. If the stars are examined at intervals of six months apart, this is equivalent to making observations from the ends of a base line almost 200 million miles long (Fig. 15), because the

Fig. 15. The annual parallax of a star is the angle p, with which the distance from the sun and earth can be calculated. The earth's positions at intervals of six months are designated E_1 and E_2. The distance E_1E_2 gives a base line of 200,000,000 miles long from which to observe the star P and obtained the angle E_1PE_2, or 2p.

radius of the earth's orbit around the sun is 93 million miles. Since Copernicus and the astronomers of his day could not determine any parallax of the fixed stars by such semiannual observations, it had to be assumed that

seen in this comparison. The dots at the inner ends of the radii of the planets' deferents (large circles) denote the centers of the orbits relative to the center of the sun's orbit in the Ptolemaic system and relative to the sun in the Copernican system. Note the use of epicycles in both systems. (After William D. Stahlman) the stars were enormously far off, if indeed the earth did move around the sun. It was far simpler to say that the absence of any observed annual parallax of the fixed stars tended to disprove the whole basis of the Copernican system.

From the failure of astronomical observation, let us turn next to the failure of mechanics. How did Copernicus explain the motion of bodies on a moving earth? These are the problems we discussed in the first chapter, none of which Copernicus explained adequately. He assumed that somehow or other the air around the earth moved with the earth, and that this air was in some way attached to the earth. It was on this assumption that he thought objects in the air were carried around as the earth moves—a kind of theory of gravity of a crude sort, but one not at all adequate to the problem.

But there was another situation some ways even more difficult to account for—the nature of the solar system itself. If Copernicus still held to the principles of Aristotelian physics—and he never invented a new physics to take the place of the Aristotelian—how could he explain that the earth seemed to move in a daily rotation and in an annual circular orbit, both of them contrary to its nature? In point of fact, Copernicus was forced to say that the earth moving around the sun was "merely another planet." But to say that the earth was "merely another planet" was to deny the Aristotelian principle that the earth and the planets are made of different materials, are subject to different sets of physical laws, and behave therefore in different ways. To argue that the earth travels in an orbit around the sun meant that the earth was undergoing violent motion. Evidently, Copernicus had an instinctive feeling that some kind of force rays emanating from the sun made the earth and the planets move together but he never elaborated this concept of force into a workable system of physics.

Those who have read Copernicus no doubt have been

puzzled further by his statement that the earth *must* have a rotation about its axis as well as a motion in a large circle around the sun, that this follows from the fact that the earth has a spherical shape. How then could Copernicus also assert that the sun, which has a spherical shape, stands still and neither rotates about its axis nor moves in an annual revolution?

One final problem of a mechanical nature that Copernicus was unable to cope with involved the moon. If the earth moves around the sun as the other planets do, and even if somehow or other falling objects can continue to fall straight down, and birds are not lost because the air is somehow or other glued to the earth, how is it possible that the moon continues to move around the earth while the earth dashes so rapidly through space? Here it was not a matter of the air's sticking to the earth, but rather of some kind of invisible thread which prevents the moon from getting lost.

Thus far we have confined our attention to two aspects of the Copernican system: the fact that it was at least as complex as the Ptolemaic system, and the fact that apparently insoluble problems of physics arose if one accepted his system. If we add to these objections some other general difficulties in the Copernican system, it may readily be seen that publication of his book in 1543 did not of itself achieve a revolution in physical or astronomical thought.

Advantages and Disadvantages of a Copernican Universe

Apart from the purely scientific problems, the concept of a moving earth created dreadfully serious uncertainties in the thought of Copernicus's day. When all is said and done, it *is* rather comforting to think that our abode is fixed in space and has a proper place in the scheme of things, rather than being an insignificant speck whirling aimlessly somewhere or other in a vast and perhaps even infinite universe. The Aristotelian uniqueness of the earth, based on its supposedly fixed position, gave man a sense of pride that could hardly arise from his being on a rather small planet (compared to Jupiter or Saturn) in a rather insignificant location (position 3 or 4 out of 7 successive planetary orbits). To say the earth is "merely another planet" suggests that it may not have even the distinction of being the only inhabited globe, and this implies that earthly man himself is not unique. And perhaps other stars are suns with other planets and on each are other kinds of man. Most men of the sixteenth century were not ready for such views, and the evidence of their senses reinforced their bias. Planet indeed! Anyone who looks at a planet —Venus, Mars, Jupiter, or Saturn—will "see" at once that it is "another star" and not "another earth." The fact that these planetary "stars" are brighter than the others, wander with respect to the others, and may have an occasional retrograde motion does not make them in any way like this earth on which we stand. And if it were not enough that all "common sense" rebels at the idea of the earth as "merely another planet," there is the evidence of Scripture. Again and again Holy Writ mentions a moving sun and a fixed earth. Even before the publication of *De revolutionibus,* Martin Luther heard about Copernicus's ideas and condemned them violently for contradicting the Bible. And everyone is well aware that Galileo's subsequent advocacy of the new system brought him into conflict with the Roman Inquisition.

It should be clear, therefore, that the alteration of the frame of the universe proposed by Copernicus could not be accomplished without shaking the whole structure of science and of man's thought about himself. But there was an attendant ferment in men's thinking about the nature of the universe, and about the earth, which was eventually to produce profound change. This is the sense in which we can date the scientific revolution at 1543. The problems posed and their implications penetrated the very foundations of physics and astronomy. From what has been said thus far, the way in which changes in one section of physical science affect the whole body of science should be clear. Practicing scientists today are familiar with this phenomenon, having witnessed the growth of modern atomic physics and quantum theory. Yet nowhere can the unity of the structure of science be seen better than in the fact that the Copernican system, whether in its simple or complex form, could not stand by itself as expounded by Copernicus. It required a modification of the currently held ideas about the nature of matter, the nature of the planets, the sun, the moon, and the stars, and the nature and actions of force in relation to motion. It has been well said that the greatness of Copernicus lay not so much in the system he propounded as in the fact that the system he did propound could ignite the great revolution in physics that we associate with the names of such as Galileo, Johannes Kepler, and Isaac Newton.

CHAPTER 4

Exploring the Depths of the Universe

The march of science has rhythms not wholly unlike those of music. As in sonatas, certain themes recur in a more or less orderly sequence of variations. The place of Copernicus in the history of science may well illustrate this process. Although his system was neither so simple nor so revolutionary as it often is represented, his book raised all the questions that had been lurking behind every cosmological scheme since antiquity. The elaborate proofs that Aristotle and Ptolemy had given of the immobility of the earth could never fully conceal from any reader that another view was possible even though Aristotle and Ptolemy had attacked it.

Evolution of the New Physics

As in any well-structured musical composition, the main Copernican theme appears in separate parts. One man in antiquity, Heracleides of Pontus, had presented the concept of a rotation of the earth, but not an orbital motion, while Aristarchus had a scheme in which the earth both rotated on its axis and revolved around the sun as the planets do. In the Latin Middle Ages prior to Copernicus it was not uncommon to find thinkers like the Frenchman Nicole Oresme and the German Nicolas Cusanus considering the possible motions of the earth, and it would have been extraordinary indeed if the theme of the moving earth did not manifest itself again after Copernicus. *De revolutionibus* contained the most complete account of a heliostatic universe ever composed, and for the specialist in astronomy and the cosmologist it proposed much that was new and important. In the same sense that the logic of a sonata leads from the original statement of a theme through successive variations, but does not dictate exactly what the variations shall be, so the logic of the development of science enables us to predict some of the consequences of the scientific revolution of 1543. But only a knowledge of history itself would reveal that the gradual acceptance of Copernican ideas by one scholar here and another there was rudely interrupted in 1609, when a new scientific instrument changed the level and the tone of discussion of the Copernican and Ptolemaic systems to such a degree that the year overshadows 1543 in the development of modern astronomy.

It was in 1609 that man began to use the telescope to make systematic studies of the heavens. The revelations proved that Ptolemy made specific errors and important ones, that the Copernican system appeared to fit the new facts of observation, and that the moon and the planets in reality were very much like the earth in a variety of different ways and were patently unlike the stars.

After 1609 any discussion of the respective merits of the two great systems of the world was bound to turn on phenomena that were beyond the ken and even the imagination of either Ptolemy or Copernicus. And once the heliocentric system was seen to have a possible basis in reality, it would spur the search for a physics that would apply with equal accuracy on a moving earth and throughout the universe. The introduction of the telescope would have been enough by itself to turn the course of science, but another development of 1609 further accelerated the revolution: Johannes Kepler published his *Astronomia nova,* which not only simplified the Copernican system by getting rid of all the epicycles but also firmly established two laws of planetary motion, as we shall see in a later chapter.

Galileo Galilei

The scientist who was chiefly responsible for introducing the telescope as a scientific instrument, and who laid the foundations of the new physics, was Galileo Galilei. In 1609 he was a professor at the University of Padua, in the Venetian Republic, and was forty-five years old, which is considerably beyond the age when most men are likely to make profoundly significant scientific discoveries. The last great Italian, except for nobles and kings, to be known to posterity by his first name, Galileo was born in Pisa, Italy, in 1564, almost on the day of Michelangelo's death and within a year of Shakespeare's birth. His father sent him to the university at Pisa, where his sardonic combativeness quickly won him the nickname "wrangler." Although his first thought had been to study medicine—it was better paid than most professions—he soon found that it was not the career for him. He discovered the beauty of mathematics and thereafter devoted his life to it, physics and astronomy. We do not know exactly when or how he became a Copernican, but on his own testimony it happened earlier than 1597.

Galileo made his first contribution to astronomy before he ever used a telescope. In 1604 a "nova" or new star suddenly appeared in the constellation Serpentarius. Galileo showed this to be a "true" star, located out in the celestial spaces and not inside the sphere of the moon. That is, Galileo found that this new star had no measurable parallax and so was very far from the earth. Thus he delivered a nice blow at the Aristotelian system of physics because he proved that change *could* occur in the heavens despite Aristotle, who had held the heavens unchangeable and had limited the region where change may occur to the earth and its surroundings. Galileo's proof seemed to him all the more decisive in that it was the second nova to be observed and found to have no measurable parallax. The previous one of 1572, in the constellation Cassiopeia, had been studied by the Danish astronomer Tycho Brahe (1546–1601), the major figure in astronomical science between Copernicus and Galileo. Among the achievements of Tycho were the design and construction of improved naked-eye instruments and the establishment of new standards of accuracy in astronomical observation. Tycho's nova, rivaling the brightness of Venus at its peak and then gradually fading away, shone for sixteen months. Since this star had no detectable parallax, and yet did not partake of planetary motion but remained in a constant orientation with respect to the other fixed stars, Tycho concluded that change may occur in the region of the fixed stars no matter what Aristotle or any of his followers had said. Tycho's observations contributed to the cumulative evidence against Aristotle, but the crushing blow had to await the night when Galileo first turned his telescope to the stars.

The Telescope: A Giant Step

The history of the telescope is itself an interesting subject. Some scholars have attempted to establish that such an instrument had been devised in the Middle Ages. Apparently an instrument like a telescope was described by Leonard Digges, who died about 1571, and a telescope with an inscription stating that it had been made in Italy in 1590 was in the possession of a Dutch scientist around 1604. What effect, if any, these early instruments had on the ultimate development of telescopes we do not know; perhaps this is an example of an invention made and then lost again. But in 1608, the instrument was re-invented in Holland, and there are at least three claimants for the honor of having then made the "first" one. Who actually deserves the credit is of little concern to us here, because our main problem is to learn how the telescope changed the course of scientific thought. Some time early in 1609 Galileo heard a report of the telescope, but without any specific information as to the way in which the instrument was constructed. He told us how:

". . . A report reached my ears that a certain Fleming had constructed a spyglass by means of which visible objects, though very distant from the eye of the observer, were distinctly seen as if nearby. Of this truly remarkable effect several experiences were related, to which some persons gave credence while others denied them. A few days later the report was confirmed to me in a letter from a noble Frenchman at Paris, Jacques Badovere [a former pupil of Galileo], which caused me to apply myself wholeheartedly to inquire into the means by which I might arrive at the invention of a similar instrument. This I did shortly afterwards, my basis being the theory of refraction. First I prepared a tube of lead, at the ends of which I fitted two glass lenses, both plane on one side while on the other side one was spherically convex and the other concave. Then placing my eye near the concave lens I perceived objects satisfactorily large and near, for they appeared three times closer and nine times larger than when seen with the naked eye alone. Next I constructed another one, more accurate, which represented objects as enlarged more than sixty times. Finally, sparing neither labor nor expense, I succeeded in constructing for myself so excellent an instrument that objects seen by means of

it appeared nearly one thousand times larger and over
thirty times closer than when regarded with our natural vision."

Galileo was not the only observer to point the new
instrument toward the heavens. It is even possible that
two observers—Thomas Harriot in England and Simon
Marius in Germany—may in some respects have been
ahead of him. But there seems to be general agreement
that the credit of first using the telescope for astronomical purposes may be given to Galileo because of "the per-
sistent way in which he examined object after object,
whenever there seemed any reasonable prospect of results following, by the energy and acuteness with which
he followed up each clue, by the independence of mind
with which he interpreted his observations, and above
all by the insight with which he realized their astronomical importance," as said Arthur Berry, British historian
of astronomy.

It is impossible to exaggerate the effects of his telescopic discoveries on Galileo's life, so profound were
they. Not only is this true of Galileo's personal life and
thought, but it is equally true of their influence on the
history of scientific thought. Galileo had the experience
of beholding the heavens as they actually are for perhaps
the first time, and wherever he looked he found evidence
to support the Copernican system against the Ptolemaic,
or at least to weaken the authority of the ancients. This
shattering experience—of observing the depths of the
universe, of being the first mortal to know what the
heavens are actually like—made so deep an impression
upon Galileo that it is only by considering the events
of 1609 in their proper proportion that one can understand the subsequent direction of his life. And it is only
in this way that we can understand how there came
about that great revolution in the science of dynamics

which may properly be said to mark the beginning of modern physics.

To see the way in which these events occurred, let us turn to Galileo's account of his discoveries, in a book which he called *Sidereus nuncius, The Starry Messenger* or *The Starry Message*. In its subtitle, the book is said to reveal "great, unusual, and remarkable spectacles, opening these to the consideration of every man, and especially of philosophers and astronomers." The newly observed phenomena, the title page of the book declared, were to be found "in the surface of the moon, in innumerable fixed stars, in nebulae, and above all in four planets swiftly revolving about Jupiter at differing distances and periods, and known to no one before the Author recently perceived them and decided that they should be named the Medicean Stars."

The Landscape of the Moon

Immediately after describing the construction and use of the telescope, Galileo turned to results. He would "review the observations made during the past two months, once more inviting the attention of all who are eager for true philosophy to the first steps of such important contemplations."

The first celestial body to be studied was the moon, the most prominent object in the heavens (except for the sun), and the one nearest to us. The crude woodcuts accompanying Galileo's text cannot convey the sense of wonder and delight this new picture of the moon awoke in him. The lunar landscape, seen through the telescope (Plates II and III), unfolds itself to us as a dead world— a world without color, and so far as the eye can tell, one without any life upon it. But the characteristic that stands out most clearly in photographs, and that so impressed Galileo in 1609, is the fact that the moon's surface looks like a ghostly *earthly* landscape. No one who looks at these photographs, and no one who looks through a telescope, can escape the feeling that the moon is a miniature earth, however dead it may appear, and that there are on it mountains and valleys, oceans, and seas with islands in them. To this day, we refer to those oceanlike regions as "maria" even though we know, as Galileo later discovered, that there is no water on the moon, and that these are not true seas at all.

The spots on the moon, whatever may have been said about them before 1609, were seen by Galileo in a coldly new and different light (Plate IV). He found "that the surface of the moon is not smooth, uniform, and precisely spherical as a great number of philosophers believe it (and the other heavenly bodies) to be, but is uneven, rough, and full of cavities and prominences, being not unlike the face of the earth, relieved by chains of mountains and deep valleys." As an example of Galileo's style in describing the earthlike quality of the moon, read the following:

"Again, not only are the boundaries of shadow and light in the moon seen to be uneven and wavy, but still more astonishingly many bright points appear within the darkened portion of the moon, completely divided and separated from the illuminated part and at a considerable distance from it. After a time these gradually increase in size and brightness, and an hour or two later they become joined with the rest of the lighted part which has now increased in size. Meanwhile more and more peaks shoot up as if sprouting now here, now there, lighting up within the shadowed portion; these become larger, and finally they too are united with that same luminous surface which extends further. And on the earth, before the rising of the sun, are not the highest peaks of the mountains illuminated by the sun's rays while the plains remain in shadow? Does not the light go on spreading while the larger

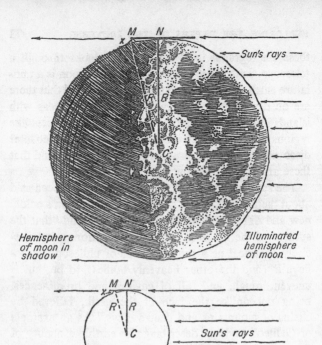

Fig. 16. Galileo's measurement of the height of mountains on the moon was simple but convincing. The point N is the terminator (boundary) between the illuminated and non-illuminated portions of moon. The point M is a bright spot observed in the shadowed region; Galileo correctly surmised that the bright spot was a mountain peak whose base remained shadowed by the curvature of the moon. He could compute the moon's radius from the moon's known distance from the earth and could estimate the distance NM through his telescope. By the Pythagorean theorem, then, $CM^2 = MN^2 + CN^2$, or, since R is the radius and x the altitude of the peak,

$$(R + x)^2 = R^2 + MN^2, \text{ or}$$
$$R^2 + 2Rx + x^2 = R^2 + MN^2, \text{ or}$$
$$x^2 + 2Rx - MN^2 = 0$$

which is easily solved for x, the altitude of the peak.

central parts of these mountains are becoming illuminated? And when the sun has finally risen, does not the illumination of plains and hills finally become one? But on the moon the variety of elevations and depressions appears to surpass in every way the roughness of the terrestrial surface, as we shall demonstrate further on."

Not only did Galileo describe the appearance of mountains on the moon; he also measured them. It is characteristic of Galileo as a scientist of the modern school that as soon as he found any kind of phenomenon he wanted to measure it. It is all very well to be told that the telescope discloses that there are mountains on the moon, just as there are mountains on the earth. But how much more extraordinary it is, and how much more convincing, to be told that there are mountains on the moon and that they are exactly four miles high! Galileo's determination of the height of the mountains on the moon has withstood the test of time, and today we agree with his estimate of their maximum height. (For those who are interested, Galileo's method of computing the height of these mountains will be found in Fig. 16.)

To see what a world of difference there was between Galileo's realistic description of the moon, which resembles the description that an aviator might give of the earth as seen from the air, and the generally prevailing view, read the following lines from Dante's *Divine Comedy*. Written in the fourteenth century, this work is generally considered to be the ultimate expression of the culture of the Middle Ages. In this part of the poem Dante has arrived on the moon and discusses certain features of it with Beatrice, who speaks to him with the "divine voice." This is how the moon appeared to this medieval space traveler:

Meseemed a cloud enveloped us, shining, dense,

firm and polished, like diamond smitten by
the sun.
Within itself the eternal pearl received us, as water
doth receive a ray of light, though still itself
uncleft. . . .

Dante asked Beatrice:

"But tell me what those dusky marks upon this
body, which down there on earth make folk
to tell the tale of Cain?"
She smiled a little, and then: "And if," she said,
"the opinion of mortals goeth wrong, where
the key of sense doth not unlock,
truly the shafts of wonder should no longer pierce
thee; since even when the senses give the lead
thou see'st reason hath wings too short. . . ."

Dante had written that man's senses deceive him, that
the moon is really eternal and perfect and absolutely
spherical, and even homogeneous. One should not trust
reason, he believed, since the mind of man is not quite
able to grasp the cosmic mysteries. Galileo, on the other
hand, trusted the revelation of the senses enlarged by
the telescope, and he concluded:

"Hence if anyone wished to revive the old Pythagorean opinion that the moon is like another earth, its
brighter part might very fitly represent the surface
of the land and its darker region that of the water.
I have never doubted that if our globe were seen
from afar when flooded with sunlight, the land regions would appear brighter and the watery regions
darker. . . ."

Apart from the statement about water, which Galileo
later corrected, what is important in this conclusion is
that Galileo saw that the surface of the moon provided

evidence that the earth is not unique. Since the moon resembles the earth, he had demonstrated that at least the nearest heavenly body does not enjoy that perfection attributed to all heavenly bodies by the classic authorities. Nor did Galileo make this a passing reference; he returned to the idea later in the book when he compared a portion of the moon to a specific region on earth: "In the center of the moon there is a cavity larger than all the rest, and perfectly round in shape. . . . As to light and shade, it offers the same appearance as would a region like Bohemia if that were enclosed on all sides by very lofty mountains arranged exactly in a circle."

Earthshine

At this point Galileo introduces a still more startling discovery: earthshine. This phenomenon may be seen in the photograph reproduced in Plate V. From the photograph it is plain, as may be seen when the moon is examined through a telescope, that there is what Galileo called a "secondary" illumination of the dark surface of the moon, which can be shown geometrically to accord perfectly with light from the sun reflected by the earth into the moon's darkened regions. It cannot be the moon's own light, or a contribution of starlight, since it would then be displayed during eclipses; it is not. Nor can it come from Venus or from any other planetary source. As for the moon's being illuminated by the earth, what, asked Galileo, is there so remarkable about this? "The earth, in fair and grateful exchange, pays back to the moon an illumination similar to that which it receives from her throughout nearly all the darkest gloom of night."

Here Galileo ends his description of the moon. The subject is one which, he told his readers, he would discuss more fully in his book on the *System of the World*. "In that book," he said, "by a multitude of arguments and experiences, the solar reflection from the earth will be shown to be quite real—against those who argue that the earth must be excluded from the dancing whirl of stars [or heavenly bodies] for the specific reason that it is devoid of motion and of light. We shall prove the earth to be a wandering body surpassing the moon in splendor, and not the sink of all dull refuse of the universe; this we shall support by an infinitude of arguments drawn from nature." This was Galileo's first announcement that he was writing a book on the system of the world, a work which was delayed for many years and which—when finally published—resulted in Galileo's trial before the Roman Inquisition.

But observe what Galileo had proved thus far. He showed that the ancients were wrong in their descriptions of the moon; the moon is not the perfect body they pictured, but resembles the earth, which therefore cannot be said to be unique and consequently different from all the heavenly objects. And if this was not enough, his studies of the moon had shown that the earth shines. No longer was it valid to say that the earth is not a shining object like the planets. And if the earth shines just as the moon does, perhaps the planets may also shine in the very same manner by reflecting light from the sun! Remember, in 1609 it was still an undecided question whether the planets shine from internal light, like the sun and the stars, or whether by reflected light, like the moon. As we shall see in a moment, it was one of Galileo's greatest discoveries to prove that the planets shine by reflected light, and that they encircle the sun in their orbits.

Stars Galore

But before turning to that subject, let us state briefly some of Galileo's other discoveries. When Galileo looked at the fixed stars, he found that they, like the planets, "appear not to be enlarged by the telescope in the same proportion as that in which it magnifies other objects, and even the moon itself." Furthermore, Galileo called attention to "the differences between the appearance of the planets and of the fixed stars" in the telescope. "The planets show their globes perfectly round and definitely bounded, looking like little moons, spherical and flooded all over with light; the fixed stars are never seen to be bounded by a circular periphery, but have rather

Fig. 17. Orion's Belt and Sword, viewed through Galileo's telescope, was seen to contain eighty more stars (the smaller ones) than could be discerned by the naked eye.

the aspect of blazes whose rays vibrate about them and scintillate a great deal." Here was the basis of one of Galileo's great answers to the detractors of Copernicus. Plainly, the stars must be at enormous distances from the earth compared to the planets, if a telescope can magnify the planets to make them look like discs, but cannot do the same with the fixed stars.

Galileo related how he "was overwhelmed by the vast quantity of stars," so many that he found "more than five hundred new stars distributed among the old ones within limits of one or two degrees of arc." To three previously known stars in Orion's Belt and six in the Sword (Fig. 17), he added "eighty adjacent stars." In several pictures he presented the results of his observations with a large number of newly discovered stars amongst the older ones. Although Galileo does not make the point explicitly, it is implied that one hardly needed to put one's faith in the ancients, since they had never seen most of the stars, and had spoken from woefully incomplete evidence. A weakness of naked-eye observation was exposed by Galileo in terms of "the nature and the material of the Milky Way." With the aid of the telescope, he wrote, the Milky Way has been "scrutinized so directly and with such ocular certainty that all the disputes which have vexed philosophers through so many ages have been resolved, and we are at last freed from wordy debates about it." Seen through the telescope, the Milky Way is "nothing but a congeries of innumerable stars grouped together in clusters. Upon whatever part of it the telescope is directed, a vast crowd of stars is immediately presented to view." And this was true not only of the Milky Way, but also of "the stars which have been called 'nebulous' by every astronomer up to this time," and which "turn out to be groups of very small stars arranged in a wonderful manner." Now for the big news:

"We have . . . briefly recounted the observations made thus far with regard to the moon, the fixed stars and the Milky Way. There remains the matter which in my opinion deserves to be considered the most important of all—the disclosure of four PLANETS never seen from the creation of the world up to our own time, together with the occasion of my having discovered and studied them, their arrangements, and the observations made of their movements and alterations during the past two months. I invite all astronomers to apply themselves to examine them and determine their periodic times, something which has so far been quite impossible to complete, owing to the shortness of the time. Once more, however, warning is given that it will be necessary to have a very accurate telescope such as we have described at the beginning of this discourse."

It is interesting to observe that Galileo called the newly discovered objects "Medicean stars," although we would call them moons or satellites of Jupiter. We must remember that in Galileo's day almost all the heavenly objects were called stars—a term which could include both the fixed stars and the wandering stars (or planets). Hence the newly discovered objects, which were "wanderers," and so a kind of planet, could also be called stars. Most of Galileo's book is, in fact, devoted to his methodical observations of Jupiter and the "stars" near it. Sometimes they were seen to the east and sometimes to the west of Jupiter, but never very far from the planet. They accompanied Jupiter "in both its retrograde and direct movements in a constant manner," so that it was evident that they were somehow connected to Jupiter.

Jupiter as Evidence

The first thoughts, that these might have been simply some new stars near which Jupiter was seen, were dispelled as Galileo observed that these newly discovered objects continued to move along with Jupiter. It was also possible for Galileo to show that the sizes of their respective orbits about Jupiter were different, and that the periodic times were likewise different. Let us allow Galileo to set forth the conclusions he drew from these observations in his own words:

> "Here we have a fine and elegant argument for quieting the doubts of those who, while accepting with tranquil mind the revolutions of the planets about the sun in the Copernican system, are mightily disturbed to have the moon alone revolve about the earth and accompany it in an annual rotation about the sun. Some have believed that this structure of the universe should be rejected as impossible. But now we have not just one planet rotating about another while both run through a great orbit around the sun; our own eyes show us four stars which wander around Jupiter as does the moon around the earth, while all together trace out a grand revolution about the sun in the space of twelve years."

Jupiter, a small-scale model of the whole Copernican system, in which four small objects move around the planet just as the planets move around the bright sun, thus answered one of the major objections to the Copernican system. Galileo could not at this point explain why it was that Jupiter could move in its orbit without losing its four encircling attendants, any more than he was ever really able to explain how the earth could move through space and not lose its one encircling moon. But whether or not he knew the reason, it was perfectly plain that in every system of the world that had ever been conceived Jupiter was considered to move in an orbit, and if it could do so and not lose four of its moons, why could not the earth move without losing a single moon? Furthermore, if Jupiter has four moons, the earth with

Plate I. "Will it fall back down again?" This old woodcut, taken from the correspondence of René Descartes, illustrates an experiment proposed by Father Mersenne, contemporary and friend of Galileo, to test the behavior of falling bodies. "*Retombera-t-il?*" the legend asks. Will the cannon ball come back down again?

Plate II. A landscape like the earth's but a *dead* one was what impressed Galileo the first time he turned his telescope to the moon.

Plate III. Galileo was the first to see the craters on the moon. His observations killed the ancient belief that the moon was smooth and perfectly spherical.

Plate IV. Galileo's own drawing of the moon is reproduced here but upside down in accordance with the practice of showing astronomical photographs. Telescopic cameras take an inverted picture.

its single moon is hardly a unique object in the heavens.

Although Galileo's book ends with the description of the satellites of Jupiter, it will be wise, before we explore the implications of his research, to discuss three other astronomical discoveries made by Galileo with his tele-

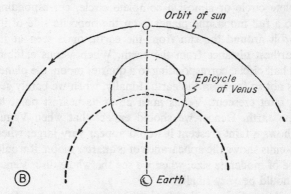

Fig. 18. The phases of Venus, first observed by Galileo, were a powerful argument against the ancient astronomy. In (A) you can see how the existence of phases accords with the system of Copernicus and how the change in the relative apparent diameter of Venus supports the concept of the planet having a solar orbit. In (B) you can see why the phenomenon would be impossible in the Ptolemaic system.

scope. The first was the discovery that Venus exhibits
phases. For a number of reasons Galileo was overjoyed
to discover that Venus exhibits phases. In the first place,
it proved that Venus shines by reflected light, and not
by a light of its own; this meant that Venus is like the
moon in this regard, and also like the earth (which
Galileo had previously shown to shine by reflected light
of the sun). Here was another point of similarity between the planets and the earth, another weakening of
the ancient philosophical barrier between earth and
heavenly objects. Furthermore, as may be seen in Fig.
18A, if Venus moves in an orbit around the sun, not only
will Venus go through a complete cycle of phases, but
under constant magnification the different phases will appear to be of different sizes because of the change in
the distance of Venus from the earth. For instance, when
Venus is at such a position as to enable us to see a complete circle or almost a complete circle, corresponding
to a full moon, the planet is on the opposite side of its
orbit around the sun from the earth, or is seen at its
farthest distance from the earth. When Venus exhibits
a half circle, corresponding to a quarter moon, the planet
is not so far from the earth. Finally, when we barely see
a faint crescent, Venus must be at its nearest point to
the earth. Hence, we should expect that when Venus
shows a faint crescent it would appear very large; when
Venus shows the appearance of a quarter moon, it would
be of moderate size; when we see the whole disc, Venus
should be very small.

According to the Ptolemaic system, Venus (like
Mercury) would never be seen far from the sun, and
hence would be observed only as morning star or evening
star near the place where the sun has either risen or set.
The center of the orbit's epicycle would be permanently
aligned between the center of the earth and the center
of the sun and would move around the earth with a
period of one year, just as the sun does. But it is per-

fectly plain, as may be seen in Fig. 18B, that in these circumstances we could never see the complete sequence of phases Galileo observed—and we can observe. For instance, the possibility of seeing Venus as a disc arises only if Venus is farther from the earth than the sun, and can never arise according to the principles of the Ptolemaic system. Here then was a most decisive blow against the Ptolemaic system.

We need not say much about two further telescopic discoveries of Galileo, because they had less force than the previous ones. The first was the discovery that sometimes Saturn appeared to have a pair of "ears," and that sometimes the "ears" changed their shape and even disappeared. Galileo never could explain this strange appearance, because his telescope could not resolve the rings of Saturn. But at least he had evidence to demonstrate how erroneous it was to speak of planets as perfect celestial objects, when they could have such queer shapes. One of his most interesting observations was of the spots on the sun, described in a book that bore the title *History and Demonstrations concerning Sunspots and their Phenomena* (1613). Not only did the appearance of these spots prove that even the sun was not the perfect celestial object described by the ancients, but Galileo was able to show that from observations of these spots one could prove the rotation of the sun, and even compute the speed with which the sun rotates upon its axis. Although the fact that the sun did rotate became extremely important in Galileo's own mechanics, it did not imply, as he seems to have believed, that annual revolution of the earth around the sun must follow.

A New World

As may be imagined, the excitement caused by these new discoveries was communicated from person to person, and the fame of Galileo spread. Naming the satellites of Jupiter "Medicean stars," had the desired effect of obtaining for Galileo the post of mathematician to Grand Duke Cosmo of the House of Medici and enabling him to return to his native Florence. The discovery of the new planets was hailed as the discovery of a new world, and Galileo acclaimed the equal of Columbus. Not only did scientists and philosophers become excited by the new discoveries, but all men of learning and wit, poets and courtiers and painters, responded in the same way. A painting by the artist Cigoli for a chapel in Rome used Galileo's telescopic discoveries concerning the moon for a motif. In a poem by Johannes Faber, Galileo receives the following praise:

> Yield, Vespucci, and let Columbus yield. Each of these
> Holds, it is true, his way through the unknown sea. . . .
> But you, Galileo, alone gave to the human race the sequence of stars,
> New constellations of heaven.

One poem in praise of Galileo's discoveries was written by Maffeo Cardinal Barberini, who later—as Pope Urban VIII—directed that Galileo be brought to trial by the Inquisition; he told Galileo that he proposed "to add lustre to my poetry by coupling it with your name." Ben Jonson wrote a masque in verse dealing with Galileo's discovery, and called it *Newes from the New World*—not the new world of America but the heavens brought near by Galileo's telescope. To gain some idea of the way in which this news was spread, read the following extract from a letter written on the day that Galileo's *Sidereus nuncius* appeared in Venice, March 13, 1610, by Sir Henry Wotton, the British Ambassador to Venice:

> "Now touching the occurrents of the present, I send herewith unto His Majesty the strangest piece of news

(as I may justly call it) that he hath ever yet received from any part of the world; which is the annexed book (come abroad this very day) of the Mathematical Professor at Padua, who by the help of an optical instrument (which both enlargeth and approximateth the object) invented first in Flanders, and bettered by himself, hath discovered four new planets rolling about the sphere of Jupiter, besides many other unknown fixed stars; likewise, the true cause of the *Via Lactae* [Milky Way], so long searched; and lastly, that the moon is not spherical, but endued with many prominences, and, which is of all the strangest, illuminated with the solar light by reflection from the body of the earth, as he seemeth to say. So as upon the whole subject he hath first overthrown all former astronomy—for we must have a new sphere to save the appearances—and next to all astrology. For the virtue of these new planets must needs vary the judicial part, and why may there not yet be more? These things I have been bold thus to discourse unto your Lordship, whereof here all corners are full. And the author runneth a fortune to be either exceeding famous or exceeding ridiculous. By the next ship your Lordship shall receive from me one of the above instruments, as it is bettered by this man."

When Kepler wrote of Galileo's discoveries in the preface to his *Dioptrics,* he sounded more like a poet than scientist: "What now, dear reader, shall we make of our telescope? Shall we make a Mercury's magic-wand to cross the liquid aether with, and like Lucian, lead a colony to the uninhabited evening star, allured by the sweetness of the place? Or shall we make it a Cupid's arrow, which, entering by our eyes, has pierced our inmost mind, and fired us with a love of Venus? . . ." Enraptured, Kepler wrote, "O telescope, instrument of much knowledge, more precious than any scepter! Is

not he who holds thee in his hand made king and lord of
the works of God?"

In 1615, James Stephens could call his mistress "my
perspective glasse, through which I view the world's
vanity." And Andrew Marvell wrote of Galileo's discovery of sun spots:

> So his bold Tube, Man, to the Sun apply'd.
> And Spots unknown to the bright Stars descry'd;
> Show'd they obscure him, while too near they please,
> And seem his Courtiers, are but his disease.
> Through Optick Trunk the Planet seem'd to hear,
> And hurls them off, e're since, in his Career.

John Milton was well aware of Galileo's discoveries.
Milton, whose views on the epicycle were quoted in
Chapter 3, stated that when he was in Italy he "found
and visited the famous Galileo, grown old a prisoner to
the Inquisition." In his *Paradise Lost,* he refers more
than once to the "glass of Galileo," or the "optic glass"
of the "Tuscan artist," and to the discoveries made with
that instrument. Writing of the moon in terms of the
other phenomena discovered by Galileo, Milton referred
to "new lands, rivers or mountains in her spotty globe";
and the discovery of the planets of Jupiter suggested that
other planets might have their attendants too: ". . .
and other Suns, perhaps with their attendant Moons,
thou wilt descry." But, apart from specific references to
Galileo's astronomical discoveries, what chiefly impressed Milton was the vastness of the universe and the
innumerable stars described by Galileo:

> . . . stars
> Numerous, and every star perhaps a world
> Of destined habitation.

This conveys the frightening thought of the immensity of
space, and the fact that the moving earth, a tiny pin-
point in this space with no fixed place, was lost.

Within a few years of the publication of Galileo's book, a sensitive reaction to it appeared in the works of the poet John Donne. Galileo's researches and discoveries crop up again and again in Donne's writings, and in particular *The Sidereal Messenger* is the subject of discussion in a work called *Ignatius His Conclave,* in which Galileo is described as he "who of late hath summoned the other world, the Stars, to come nearer to him, and give him an account of themselves." Later Donne refers to "Galilæo, the Florentine . . . who by this time hath thoroughly instructed himselfe of all the hills, woods, and Cities in the new world, the Moone. And since he effected so much with his first Glasses, that he saw the Moone, in so neere a distance that hee gave himselfe satisfaction of all, and the least parts in her, when now being growne to more perfection in his Art, he shall have made new Glasses, and . . . he may draw the Moone, like a boate floating upon the water, as neere the earth as he will."

Prior to 1609 the Copernican system had seemed to men a mere mathematical speculation, a proposal made to "save the phenomenon." The basic supposition that the earth was "merely another planet" had been so contrary to all the dictates of experience and common sense that very few men had faced up to the awesome consequences of the heliostatic system. But after 1609, when men discovered through Galileo's eyes what the universe was like, they had to accept the fact that the telescope showed the world to be non-Ptolemaic and non-Aristotelian, in that the uniqueness attributed to the earth (and the physics based on that supposed uniqueness) could not fit the facts. There were only two possibilities open: One was to refuse to look through the telescope or to refuse to accept what one saw when one did; the other was to reject the physics of Aristotle and the astronomy of Ptolemy.

In this book we are more concerned with the rejection of the Aristotelian physics than we are with the rejection of the Ptolemaic astronomy, except that one went with the other. Aristotelian physics, as we have seen, was based on two postulates which could not stand the Copernican assault: One was the immobility of the earth; the other was the distinction between the physics of the earthly four elements and the physics of the fifth celestial element. So we may understand that after 1610 it became increasingly clear that the old physics had to be abandoned, and a new physics established—a physics suitable for the moving earth required in the Copernican system.*

For most thinking men in the decades following Galileo's observations with the telescope the concern was not so much for the need of a new system of physics, as it was for a new system of the world. Gone forever was the concept that the earth had a fixed spot in the center of the universe, but it was now conceived to be in motion, never in the same place for any two immediately successive instants. Gone also was the comforting thought that the earth is unique, that it is an individual object without any likeness anywhere in the universe, that the uniqueness of man had given a uniqueness to his habitation. There were other problems that soon arose, of which one is the size of the universe. For the

* Galileo's observations of the phases and relative sizes of Venus, and of the occasional gibbous phase of Mars, proved that Venus and presumably the other planets move in orbits around the sun. There is no planetary observation by which we on earth can prove that the earth is moving in an orbit around the sun. Thus all Galileo's discoveries with the telescope can be accommodated to the system invented by Tycho Brahe just before Galileo began his observations of the heavens. In this Tychonic system, the planets Mercury, Venus, Mars, Jupiter and Saturn move in orbits around the sun, while the sun moves in an orbit around the earth in a year. Furthermore, the daily rotation of the heavens is communicated to the sun and planets, so that the earth itself neither rotates nor revolves in an orbit. The Tychonic system appealed to those who sought to save the immobility of the earth while accepting some of the Copernican innovations.

ancients the universe was finite, each of the celestial spheres, including that of the fixed stars, being a finite size and moving in its diurnal motion so that each part of it had a finite speed. If the stars were at an infinite distance, then they could not move in a daily circular motion around the earth with a finite speed, for the path of an object at an infinite distance must be infinitely long, and the time it takes to move an infinite distance is infinite. Hence in the geostatic system the fixed stars could not be infinitely far away. But in the Copernican system, when the fixed stars were not only fixed with regard to one another but were actually considered fixed in space, there was no limitation upon their distance.

Not all Copernicans considered the universe infinite, and Copernicus himself certainly thought of the universe as finite, as did Galileo. But others saw Galileo's discoveries as indicating the presence of innumerable stars at infinite distances, and the earth itself diminished to a speck. Nowhere can one see the disruption of "this little world of man," and what has been called "the realization of how slight a part that world plays in an enlarged and enlarging universe," better than in these lines of a sensitive clergyman and poet, John Donne:

> And new Philosophy calls all in doubt,
> The Element of fire is quite put out;
> The Sun is lost, and th' earth, and no mans wit
> Can well direct him where to looke for it.
> And freely men confesse that this world's spent,
> When in the Planets, and the Firmament
> They seeke so many new; then see that this
> Is crumbled out againe to his Atomies.
> 'Tis all in peeces, all cohaerence gone;
> All just supply, and all Relation.

CHAPTER 5

Toward an Inertial Physics

After the second decade of the seventeenth century, the reality of the Copernican system was no longer an idle speculation. Copernicus himself, understanding the nature of his arguments, had stated quite explicitly, in the preface to *On the Revolutions of the Celestial Spheres,* that "mathematics is for the mathematicians." Another preface, unsigned, emphasized the disavowal. Inserted in the book by Osiander, a German clergyman into whose hands the printing had been entrusted, the second preface said that the Copernican system was not presented for debate on its truth or falsity, but merely as another computing device. This was all very well until Galileo made his discoveries with the telescope; then it became urgent to solve the problems of the physics of an earth in motion. Galileo devoted a considerable portion of his intellectual energy toward this end, and with a fruitful result, for he laid the foundations of the science of modern dynamics. He tried to solve two separate problems: first, to account for the behavior of falling bodies on a moving earth, falling exactly as they would appear to do if the earth were at rest, and, second, to establish new principles for the motion of falling bodies in general.

Uniform Linear Motion

Let us begin by a consideration of a limited problem: that of uniform linear motion. By this is meant motion proceeding in a straight line in such a way that if any two equal intervals of time are chosen, the distance covered in those two intervals will always be identical. This is the definition Galileo gave in his last and perhaps greatest book, *Discourses and Demonstrations Concerning Two New Sciences,* published in 1638, after his trial and condemnation by the Roman Inquisition. In this book Galileo presented his most mature views on dynamics, force in relation to motion. He emphasized particularly the fact that in defining uniform motion, it is important to make sure that the word "any" is included, for otherwise, he said, the definition would be meaningless. In this he was certainly criticizing some of his contemporaries and predecessors, and deservedly.

Suppose that there is such a motion in nature; we may ask with Galileo, what experiments could we imagine to demonstrate its nature? If we are in a ship or carriage moving uniformly in a straight line, what actually will happen to a weight allowed to fall freely? The answer, experiment will prove, is that in such circumstances the falling will be straight downward with regard to the frame of reference (say the cabin of a ship, or the interior of a carriage), and it will be so whether that frame of reference is standing still with regard to the outside environment or moving forward in a straight line at constant speed. Expressing it differently, we may state the general conclusion that no experiment can be performed within a sealed room moving in a straight line at constant speed that will tell you whether you are standing still or moving. In actual experience, we can often tell whether we are standing still or moving, because we can see from a window whether there is any relative motion between us and the earth. If the room is not closely

sealed, we may feel the air rushing through and creating
a wind. Or we may feel the vibration of motion or hear
the wheels turning in a carriage, automobile, or railroad
car. A form of relativity is involved here, and it was
stated very clearly by Copernicus, because it was essential to his argument to establish that when two objects,
such as the sun and earth, move relative to each other, it
is impossible to tell which one is at rest and which one is
in motion. Copernicus could point to the example of two
ships at harbor, one pulling away from the other. A man
on a ship asks which of the two, if either, is at anchor
and which is moving out with the tide? The only way
to tell is to observe the land, or a third ship at anchor.
In present-day terms, we could use for this example two
railroad trains on parallel tracks facing in opposite directions. We all have had the experience of watching a
train on the adjacent track and thinking that we are in
motion, only to find when the other train has left the
station that we have been at rest all the time.

A Locomotive's Smokestack and a Moving Ship

But before we discuss this point further, an experiment is in order. This demonstration makes use of a toy
train traveling along a straight track with what closely
approximates uniform motion. The locomotive's smokestack contains a small cannon actuated by a spring, so
constructed that it can fire a steel ball or marble vertically into the air. When the gun is loaded and the spring
set, a release underneath the locomotive actuates a small
trigger. In the first part of this experiment the train remains in place upon the track. The spring is set, the ball
is placed in the small cannon, and the release mechanism
triggered. In Plate VIA, a scene of successive stroboscopic shots shows us the position of the ball at equally
separated intervals. Observe that the ball travels straight
upward, reaches its maximum, then falls straight down-

ward onto the locomotive, thus striking almost the very point from which it had been shot. In the second experiment the train is set into uniform motion, and the spring once again released. Plate VIB shows what happens. A comparison of the two pictures will convince you, incidentally, that the upward and downward part of the motion is the same in both cases, and is independent of whether the locomotive is at rest or has a forward motion. We shall come back to this later in the chapter, but for the present we are primarily concerned with the fact that the ball continued to move in a forward direction with the train, and that it fell onto the locomotive just as it did when the train was at rest. Plainly then, this particular experiment, at least to the extent of determining whether the ball returns to the cannon or not, will never tell us whether the train is standing still or moving in a straight line with a constant speed.

Even those who cannot explain this experiment can draw a most important conclusion. Galileo's inability to explain how Jupiter could move without losing its satellites did not destroy the phenomenon's effectiveness as an answer to those who asked how the earth could move and not lose its moon. Just so our train experiment— even if unexplainable—would be sufficient answer to the argument that the earth must be at rest because otherwise a dropped ball would not fall vertically downward to strike the ground at a point directly below, and a cannon ball shot vertically upward would never return to the cannon.

It should be observed, and this is an important point to which we shall return, that the experiment we have just described is not exactly related to the true situation of a moving earth, because in the earth's daily rotation each point on its surface is moving in a circle while in its annual orbit the earth is traveling along a gigantic ellipse. It is nevertheless true that for ordinary experiments, in which the falling motion would usually occupy

only a few seconds, or at most a few minutes, the departure of the motion of any point on the earth from a
straight line is small enough to be insignificant.

Galileo would have nodded in approval at our experiment. In his day the experiment was discussed, but
not often performed. The usual reference frame was a
moving ship. This was a traditional problem, which
Galileo introduced in his famous *Dialogue Concerning
the Two Chief World Systems,* as a means of confuting
the Aristotelian beliefs. In the course of this discussion,
Galileo has Simplicio, the character in the dialogue who
stands for the traditional Aristotelian, say that in his
opinion an object dropped from the mast of a moving
ship will strike the ship somewhere behind the mast
along the deck. On first questioning, Simplicio admits
that he has never performed the experiment, but he is
persuaded to say that he assumes that Aristotle or one of
the Aristotelians must have done this experiment or it
would not have been reported. Ah no, says Galileo, this
is certainly a false assumption, because it is plain that
they have never performed this experiment. How can he
be so sure? asks Simplicio, and he receives this reply:
The proof that this experiment was never performed lies
in the fact that the wrong answer was obtained. Galileo
has given the right answer. The object will fall at the
foot of the mast, and it will do so whether the ship is in
motion or whether the ship is at rest. Incidentally,
Galileo asserted elsewhere that he had performed such
an experiment, although he did not say so in his treatise.
Instead he said, "I, without observation, know that the
result must be as I say, because it is necessary."

Why is it that an object falls to the same spot on the
deck from the mast of a ship that is at rest and from the
mast of a ship that is moving in a straight line with constant speed? For Galileo it was not enough that this
should be so; it required some principle that would be

basic to a system of dynamics that could account for the phenomena observed on a moving earth.

Galileo's Dynamics

Our toy train experiment, to which we shall refer again in the last chapter, illustrates three major aspects of Galileo's work in dynamics. In the first place, there is the principle of inertia, toward which Galileo strove but which, as we shall see in the final chapter, awaited the genius of Isaac Newton for its modern definitive formulation. Secondly, the photographs of the distances of descent of the ball after successive equal intervals of time illustrate his principles of uniformly accelerated motion. Finally, in the fact that the rate of downward fall during the forward motion is the same as the rate of downward fall at rest, we may see an example of Galileo's famous principle of the composition of velocities.

We shall examine these three topics by first considering Galileo's studies of accelerated motion in general, then his work dealing with inertia, and finally his analysis of complex motions.

In studying the problem of falling bodies, Galileo, we know, made experiments in which he dropped objects from heights, and—notably in the Pisan days of his youth —from a tower. Whether the tower was the famous Leaning Tower of Pisa or some other tower we cannot say; the records that he kept merely tell us that it was from some tower or other. Later on his biographer Viviani, who knew Galileo during his last years, told a fascinating story which has since taken root in the Galileo legend. According to Viviani, Galileo, desiring to confute Aristotle, ascended the Leaning Tower of Pisa, "in the presence of all other teachers and philosophers and of all students," and "by repeated experiments" proved "that the velocity of moving bodies of the same composition, unequal in weight, moving through the same medium, do not attain the proportion of their weight, as Aristotle assigned it to them, but rather that they move with equal velocity. . . ." Since there is no record of this public demonstration in any other source, scholars have tended to doubt that it happened, especially since in its usual telling and retelling it becomes fancier each time. Whether Viviani made it up, or whether Galileo told it to him in his old age, not really remembering what had happened many decades earlier, we do not know. But the fact of the matter is that the results do not agree with those given by Galileo himself because, as we mentioned in an earlier chapter, Galileo pointed out very carefully that bodies of unequal size do not attain quite the same velocity, the heavier member of the pair striking the ground a little before the lighter.

Such an experiment, if performed, could only have the result of proving Aristotle wrong. In Galileo's day, it was hardly a great achievement to prove that Aristotle was wrong in only one respect. Pierre de la Ramée (or Ramus) had some decades earlier made it known that everything in Aristotle's physics was unscientific. The inadequacies of the Aristotelian law of motion had been evident for at least four centuries, and during that time a considerable body of criticism had piled up. Although they struck another blow at Aristotle, experiments from the tower, whether the Tower of Pisa or any other, certainly did not disclose to Galileo a new and correct law of falling bodies. Yet formulation of the law was one of his greatest achievements.

To appreciate the full nature of Galileo's discoveries, we must understand the importance of abstract thinking, of its use by Galileo as a tool that in its ultimate polish was a much more revolutionary instrument than even the telescope. Galileo showed how abstraction may be related to the world of experience, how from thinking about "the nature of things," one may derive laws related to direct observation. To see how he did this, let us outline the main stages of his thought processes, as he described them to us in *Discourses and Demonstrations Concerning Two New Sciences.*

Galileo says:

"There is, in nature, perhaps nothing older than motion, concerning which the books written by philosophers are neither few nor small; nevertheless I have discovered some properties of it which are worth knowing and which have not hitherto been either observed or demonstrated."

Galileo recognized that others, too, had observed that the "natural motion of a heavy falling body is continuously accelerated." But he said that it was his achievement to find out "to just what extent this acceleration occurs." He was proud that it was he who had found for the first time "that the distances traversed during equal intervals of time by a body falling from rest stand to one another in the same ratio as the odd numbers beginning with unity." He also proved that "missiles and projectiles" do not merely describe "a curved path of some sort"; the path in fact is a parabola.

First, Galileo discusses the laws of uniform motion, in which the distance is proportional to the time and the speed therefore constant. Then he turns to accelerated motion. "To find and explain a definition best fitting natural phenomena," he calls the major primary problem. Anyone may "invent an arbitrary type of motion," he says, but it was his ambition "to consider the phenomena of bodies falling with an acceleration such as actually occurs in nature and to make this definition of accelerated motion exhibit the essential features of observed accelerated motions." Galileo says furthermore that "in the investigation of naturally accelerated motion we were led, by the hand as it were, in following the habit and custom of nature herself, in all her various other processes, to employ only those means which are

most common, simple and easy." Galileo was invoking
a famous principle here, one that actually goes back to
Aristotle, that nature always works in the simplest way
possible, or in the most economical fashion. Galileo
says:

> "When . . . I observe a stone initially at rest fall-
> ing from an elevated position and continually acquir-
> ing new increments of speed, why should I not believe
> that such increases occur in a manner which is ex-
> ceedingly simple and rather obvious to everybody? If
> now we examine the matter carefully, we find no ad-
> dition or increment more simple than that which re-
> peats itself always in the same manner."

Proceeding on the principle that nature is simple, so
that the simplest change is one in which the change itself is constant, Galileo states that if there is an equal
increment of speed in each successive interval of time,
this is plainly the simplest possible accelerated motion.
Shortly thereafter, Galileo has Simplicio (the Aristotelian) say that he holds to a different belief, namely, that
a falling body has a "velocity increasing in proportion
to the space," and we as critical readers must admit it is
certainly as "simple" as Galileo's definition of accelerated motion. Of the two possibilities

$$V \propto T \qquad\qquad (1)$$

$$V \propto D \qquad\qquad (2)$$

which is simpler? Are not both examples of "an increment . . . which repeats itself always in the same manner," either the same increment in speed in equal time
intervals or the same increment in equal spaces? They
are equally simple because both are equations of the first
degree, both examples of a simple proportionality. Both
are therefore much simpler than any of the six possibilities which follow:

$$V \propto \frac{1}{T} \tag{3}$$

$$V \propto \frac{1}{T^2} \tag{4}$$

$$V \propto T^2 \tag{5}$$

$$V \propto \frac{1}{D} \tag{6}$$

$$V \propto \frac{1}{D^2} \tag{7}$$

$$V \propto D^2 \tag{8}$$

On what possible ground can we reject the relationship suggested by Simplicio and given in Equation (2)? Since each of Equations (1) and (2) is formally as simple as the other, Galileo is forced to introduce another criterion for his choice. He asserts that possibility No. 2 —the speed increases in proportion to the distance fallen —will lead to a logical inconsistency, while the relationship given in Equation (1) does not. Hence it would appear that since one of the "simple" assumptions leads to an inconsistency, while the other does not, the only possibility is that falling bodies have speeds which increase in proportion to the time in which they have fallen.

This conclusion, as presented in Galileo's last and most mature work, has a special interest for the historian, because the argument whereby Galileo "proves" that a logical inconsistency follows from Equation (2) contains an error. There is no "logical" inconsistency here; the problem is merely that this relation is incompatible with the assumption of a body starting from rest. The historian is also interested to discover that earlier in his life Galileo wrote about this very same subject in a wholly different way to his friend Fra Paolo Sarpi. In this letter Galileo assumed that the correct law of freely falling bodies is that the speed increases in direct proportion to the distance fallen. From this assumption, Galileo wrongly believed that he could deduce that the distance fallen must be proportional to the square of the time, or that the assumption of Equation (2) leads to the equation

$$D \propto T^2 \qquad (9)$$

Then Galileo goes on to say that the proportionality of the distance to the square of the time is "well known." Between writing the letter to Sarpi, and the appearance of *The Two New Sciences,* Galileo had corrected his error.

In any event, Galileo proves that the relationship shown in Equation (9) follows from Equation (1). Galileo does so by means of an ancillary theorem as follows:

"Theorem I, Proposition I. The time in which any space is traversed by a body starting from rest and uniformly accelerated is equal to the time in which that same space would be traversed by the same body moving at a uniform speed whose value is the mean of the highest speed and the speed just before acceleration began."

By using this theorem, and the theorems on uniform motion, Galileo proceeds to

"Theorem II, Proposition II. The spaces described by a body falling from rest with a uniformly accelerated motion are to each other as the squares of the time-intervals employed in traversing these distances."

This is the result expressed in Equation (9), and it leads to Corollary 1. In this corollary Galileo shows that if a body falls from rest with uniformly accelerated motion, then the spaces $D_1, D_2, D_3, \ldots$ which are traversed in successive equal intervals of time "will bear to one another the same ratio as the series of odd numbers,

1, 3, 5, 7. . . ." Galileo is quick to point out that this series of odd numbers is derived from the fact that the distances gone in the first time interval, the first two time intervals, the first three time intervals . . . are as the squares, 1, 4, 9, 16, 25 . . . ; the differences between them are the odd numbers. The conclusion is of a special interest to us, because it was part of the Platonic tradition to believe that the fundamental truths of nature were disclosed in the relations of regular geometrical figures and relations between numbers, a point of view to which Galileo expresses his devotion in an earlier part of the book. He has Simplicio say: "Believe me, if I were again beginning my studies, I should follow the advice of Plato and start with mathematics, a science which proceeds very cautiously and admits nothing is established until it has been rigidly demonstrated." To Galileo it is evidently a token of the soundness of his discussion of falling bodies that he may conclude: "While, therefore, during equal intervals of time the velocities increase as the natural numbers, the increments in the distances traversed during these equal time-intervals are to one another as the odd numbers beginning with unity."

Although the numerical aspect of the investigation is satisfying to Salviati, the character in *The Two New Sciences* who speaks for Galileo, and to Sagredo, the man of general education and good will who usually supports Galileo, Galileo recognizes that this Platonic point of view can hardly satisfy an Aristotelian. Galileo, therefore, has Simplicio say: "I am convinced that matters are as described, once having accepted the definition of uniformly accelerated motion. But as to whether this acceleration is that which one meets in nature in the case of falling bodies, I am still doubtful; and it seems to me, not only for my own sake but also for all those who think as I do, that this would be the proper moment to introduce one of those experiments—and there are many of them, I understand—which illustrate in several ways the conclusions reached." Galileo then goes on to describe a famous experiment. Let us allow him to tell it in his own words:

"A piece of wooden moulding or scantling, about 12 cubits long, half a cubit wide, and three finger-breadths thick, was taken; on its edge was cut a channel a little more than one finger in breadth; having made this groove very straight, smooth, and polished, and having lined it with parchment, also as smooth and polished as possible, we rolled along it a hard, smooth, and very round bronze ball. Having placed this board in a sloping position, by lifting one end some one or two cubits above the other, we rolled the ball, as I was just saying, along the channel, noting, in a manner presently to be described, the time required to make the descent. We repeated this experiment more than once in order to measure the time with an accuracy such that the deviation between two observations never exceeded one-tenth of a pulse-beat. Having performed this operation and having assured ourselves of its reliability, we now rolled the ball only one-quarter the length of the channel; and having measured the time of its descent, we found it precisely one-half of the former. Next we tried other distances, comparing the time for the whole length with that for the half, or with that for two-thirds, or three-fourths, or indeed for any fraction; in such experiments, repeated a full hundred times, we always found that the spaces traversed were to each other as the squares of the times, and this was true for all inclinations of the plane, i.e., of the channel, along which we rolled the ball. We also observed that the times of descent, for various inclinations of the plane, bore to one another precisely that ratio which, as we shall see later, the Author had predicted and demonstrated for them.

"For the measurement of time, we employed a large vessel of water placed in an elevated position; to the bottom of this vessel was soldered a pipe of small diameter giving a thin jet of water, which we collected in a small glass during the time of each descent, whether for the whole length of the channel or for a part of its length; the water thus collected was weighed, after each descent, on a very accurate balance; the differences and ratios of these weights gave us the differences and ratios of the times, and this with such accuracy that although the operation was repeated many, many times, there was no appreciable discrepancy in the results."

To this Simplicio replies: "I would like to have been present at these experiments; but feeling confidence in the care with which you performed them, and in the fidelity with which you relate them, I am satisfied and accept them as true and valid."

Galileo's procedure, such as we have been describing, resembles that used by the most successful scientists, but differs radically from what is commonly described in elementary textbooks as *the* scientific method." For in all such accounts, the first step is said to be to "collect all the relevant information," and so on. The usual method of procedure, we are told, is to collect a large number of observations, or to perform a series of experiments, then to classify the results, generalize them, search for a mathematical relation, and, finally, to find a law. But Galileo proceeds by sitting at his desk with a pencil and paper, by thinking, and by creating ideas. He begins with a fundamental conviction that nature is simple, that it is a valid procedure to speculate upon the abstractions of nature, to seek the simple number relationships of the first degree rather than for those of higher order, and to find the simplest relationship that does not lead to a contradiction. The experiment is re-

lated in reply to the demands of the Aristotelians, his
critics. And it is introduced by a paragraph which it will
be profitable for us to examine in a little detail:

"The request which you, as a man of science, make,
is a very reasonable one; for this is a custom—and
properly so—in those sciences where mathematical
demonstrations are applied to natural phenomena, as
is seen in the case of perspective, astronomy, mechanics, music, and others where the principles, once
established by well-chosen experiments, become the
foundations of the entire superstructure. I hope therefore it will not appear to be a waste of time if we
discuss at considerable length this first and most fundamental question upon which hinge numerous consequences of which we have in this book only a
small number, placed there by the Author, who has
done so much to open a pathway hitherto closed to
minds of speculative turn. So far as experiments go
they have not been neglected by the Author; and
often, in his company, I have attempted in the following manner to assure myself that the acceleration
actually experienced by falling bodies is that above
described."

It is certainly made clear in this statement that the
purpose of observations or experiments, such as the inclined plane experiment, was not to find the law in its
original discovery, but simply to make certain that in
fact such accelerations as Galileo discussed may actually occur in nature. Observe, furthermore, that in point
of fact what is demonstrated in such a series of experiments or observations is not that speed is proportional
to time, but only that distance is proportional to the
square of the time. Since this is a result *implied* by
speed's being proportional to time, it is assumed that
the experiment also justifies the principle that speed is
proportional to time.

And it is further to be noted that in introducing the experiments, Salviati says that he himself had made this particular set of observations in Galileo's company "to assure myself that the acceleration actually experienced by falling bodies is that above described." And yet this particular set of observations of balls rolling down inclined planes does not apparently have anything to do with acceleration of freely falling bodies. In these experiments the falling effect of gravity is "diluted," and it is found that distance is proportional to the square of the time at any inclination one may give the plane, however steep. The experiments are related to free fall because it may be assumed that in the limiting case, in which the plane is vertical, one can expect the law still to hold. But in that limiting case of free fall the ball will not roll in its downward movement, as it does along an inclined plane—a point which Galileo nowhere mentions. And yet this is a most important condition, because we know today from theoretical mechanics that this is a chief factor that would prevent the experiments described by Galileo from proceeding in the way in which Galileo described them. He certainly idealized the conditions of his experiment when he reported that in all circumstances "there was no appreciable discrepancy in the results" or that "the times of descent, for various inclinations of the plane, bore to one another precisely that ratio which . . . the Author had predicted and demonstrated for them." The accuracy of the experiment was "such that the deviation between two observations never exceeded one-tenth of a pulse-beat."

Galileo never computed the acceleration of a freely falling body by taking the limit of motion on an inclined plane. He *said* that he had timed a freely falling body dropped from a tower. An iron ball weighing one hundred pounds, he said, "in repeated experiments falls from a height of one hundred yards in five seconds." These data contain an error of about 100 per cent. We may well understand that when one of Galileo's contemporaries, Father Mersenne, tried to repeat these experiments, he found that he could never get the same result that Galileo had reported. He could only conclude that Galileo either had not made the experiments, or had not reported the results accurately.

In retrospect it is clear to us that Galileo was using the experiment of the inclined plane only as a kind of rough check to see whether the principles that he had derived by the method of abstraction and mathematics actually applied in the world of nature. So far as he was concerned, the truth of his law of falling bodies was guaranteed by its exemplification of the simplicity of nature and the relations of integers, and not merely by a series of experiments or observations.

Galileo was here displaying the same attitude as in his discussion of the falling of an object from the mast of a ship, where again it was the nature of things and necessary relations which counted, rather than particular sets of experiences. The correct result is to be maintained, according to Galileo, even in the face of evidence from the senses (in a form of experiments or observations) which may be antagonistic. Nowhere did Galileo express this point of view more strongly than in discussing the evidence of the senses against the motion of the earth. "For the arguments against the whirling of the earth which we have already examined are very plausible, as we have seen," Galileo wrote, "and the fact that the Ptolemaics and Aristotelians and all their disciples took them to be conclusive is indeed a strong argument of their effectiveness. But the experiences which openly contradict the annual movement are indeed so much greater in their apparent force that, I repeat, there is no limit to my astonishment when I reflect that Aristarchus and Copernicus were able to make reason so conquer sense that, in defiance of the latter, the former became mistress of their belief."

To recapitulate, Galileo demonstrated mathematically that a motion starting from rest in which the speed undergoes the same change in every equal interval of time (called *uniformly accelerated motion*) corresponds to traversing distances which are proportional to the squares of the elapsed times. Then Galileo showed by experiment that this ideal law is—within certain limits, we must interject—exemplified by motion on an inclined plane. From these two results, Galileo reasoned that in the absence of any air resistance, the motion of a freely falling body will always be accelerated according to this law. If Galileo did present this result to us as being more exactly confirmed in his inclined plane experiment than observations could possibly warrant, surely we can forgive him for allowing enthusiasm to overpower the accuracy of his recollection. When Robert Boyle, some thirty years later, was able to evacuate a cylinder, he showed that in such a vacuum all bodies fall with identical speeds no matter what their shapes. Thus proof was given of Galileo's assertion—an extrapolation from experience—that but for air resistance, all bodies fall at the same rate, with the same acceleration. Today we know the correct value of this acceleration (g) to be about 32 feet per second change of speed in each second. Hence, the speed of a falling body except for the almost negligible factor of air resistance, depends only on the length of time during which it falls and not on its weight or the force moving it, as Aristotle had supposed. This result, the correct analysis of free fall, is often held to be one of Galileo's major achievements in physics. How much of it originated with Galileo?

Galileo's Predecessors

If we are to appreciate the stature of Galileo properly, we must measure him alongside his contemporaries and predecessors. When, in the final chapter, we see how

Newton depended on Galileo's achievement, we shall gain some comprehension of his historical importance. But at this point we shall see exactly how significant he was by making a more realistic appraisal of his originality than is to be found in most textbooks and in all too many histories.

Recall that it was a feature of late Greek (Alexandrian and Byzantine) physics to criticize Aristotle rather than to accept his every word as if it were absolute truth. The same critical spirit characterized Islamic scientific thought and the writings of the medieval Latin West. Thus Dante, whose works are often held to be the acme of medieval European culture, criticized Aristotle for believing "that there were no more than eight heavens [spheres]" and that "the heaven [sphere] of the sun came next after that of the moon, that is, that it was the second from us."

Scholars subjected the Aristotelian law of motion to various corrections, of which the chief features were: (1) concentration on the gradual stages by which motion changes, i.e., acceleration; (2) recognition that in describing changing motion, one can speak only of the speed at some given instant; (3) careful definition of uniform motion—a condition described in a summary of 1369 (by John of Holland) as one in which "the body traverses an equal space in every equal part of the time" *in omni parte equali temporis* (which contradicts Galileo's statement on page 95 f. that he was the first so to define uniform motion); (4) recognition that accelerated motion could be of either a uniform or nonuniform kind, as diagrammed in the following schema:

Motion {
    uniform motion
    or
    nonuniform motion
    (accelerated)
} {
    uniformly accelerated motion
    or
    nonuniformly accelerated motion
}

In his presentation Galileo went through this very type of analysis. The simplest motion, he said, is uniform (which he defined in the manner of the scholastics of the fourteenth century); next comes accelerated motion, which may be either uniformly accelerated or nonuniformly accelerated. He chose the simpler, and then explored whether the acceleration is uniform with respect to time or to distance.

In considering how speed may change uniformly the schoolmen of the fourteenth century proved what is sometimes known as the "mean speed rule." It states that the effect (distance) of a uniformly accelerated motion during any time-interval is exactly the same as if during that interval the moving body had been subject to a uniform motion that was the mean of the accelerated motion. Let us now see this rule expressed in symbols. During time T, suppose a body to be uniformly accelerated from some initial speed V_1 to a final speed V_2. How far (D) will it go? To find the answer determine the average speed $\overline{V}$ during the time-interval; then the distance D is the same as if the body had gone at a constant speed $\overline{V}$ during time T, or $D = \overline{V}T$. Furthermore, since the motion is an example of uniform acceleration, the average speed $\overline{V}$ during the time-interval is the mean of the initial and terminal speeds, so that

$$\overline{V} = \frac{V_1 + V_2}{2}$$

This is precisely the theorem used by Galileo to prove his own law relating distance to time in accelerated motion. How did the men of the fourteenth century prove it? The first proofs were produced in Merton College, Oxford, by a kind of "word algebra," but in Paris Nicole Oresme proved the theorem geometrically, using the very same diagram (Fig. 19) as Galileo!

The only major difference between Galileo's presentation and Oresme's is that the latter's was couched in

terms of any changing "quality" that might be quanti-
fied—including such physical "qualities" as speed, dis-
placement, temperature, whiteness, heaviness, etc., but
also such nonphysical "qualities" as love, charity, and
grace. But there is no instance in which these men of
the fourteenth century tested their results as Galileo did

*Fig. 19. Nicole Oresme of Paris used geometry to
prove that a body uniformly accelerated from an initial
speed V_1 to a final speed V_2 would travel the same
distance D in the time interval T that it would if it had
moved at the constant speed $\overline{V}$, the mean between V_1
and V_2. He assumed that the area under the graph of
speed plotted against time would be the distance D.
For the uniformly accelerated motion, the graph would
be an inclined line and for uniform motion the
horizontal line. The area under the first would
be the area of a triangle or $\frac{1}{2}T \times V_2$. The area of the
second would be the area of the rectangle or $T \times \frac{1}{2}V_2$,
the height of the triangle being twice that of the rectangle. The areas, and therefore the distances traveled,
would be equal.*

in order to see whether they applied to the real world
of experience. For these men the logical exercise of proving the "mean speed rule" was of itself a satisfying experience. For instance, the scientists of the fourteenth
century, so far as we know, never even explored the
possibility that two objects of unequal weight would fall
practically together. Yet, although the fourteenth century scholastics who discovered the "mean speed rule"

did not themselves apply the concept of an acceleration uniform in time to falling bodies as such, their successors did. By the time of the sixteenth century the statement that the speed of falling bodies increases continuously as a function of the time was printed again and again in the widely used book of the Spaniard Domenico de Soto, in which the "mean speed rule" was readily available.

Another medieval concept of importance in understanding the scientific thought of Galileo is "impetus." This is a property which was supposed to keep things like projectiles moving after they have left the "projector." Impetus resembles both momentum and kinetic energy, and really has no exact equivalent in modern dynamics. It was a distant ancestor of Galileo's concept of inertia and from that developed in turn the modern Newtonian view.

Galileo's originality was therefore different from what he boastfully declared. No longer need we believe anything so absurd as that there had been no progress in understanding motion between the time of Aristotle and Galileo. And we may ignore the many accounts that make it appear that Galileo invented modern dynamics with no debt to any medieval or ancient predecessor.

This was a point of view encouraged by Galileo himself but it is one that could be more justifiably held fifty years ago than today. One of the most fruitful areas of research in the history of science in the last half century —begun chiefly by the French scholar and scientist Pierre Duhem—has been the "exact sciences" of the Middle Ages. These investigations have uncovered a tradition of criticism of Aristotle which paved the way for Galileo's own contributions. By making precise exactly what Galileo owed to his predecessors, we may delineate more accurately his own heroic proportions. In this way, furthermore, we may make the life story of Galileo more real, because we are aware that in the advance of the sciences each man builds on the work of his predecessors. Never was this aspect of the scientific enterprise put better than in the following words of Lord Rutherford (1871-1937), founder of nuclear physics:

> ". . . . It is not in the nature of things for any one man to make a sudden violent discovery; science goes step by step, and every man depends on the work of his predecessors. When you hear of a sudden unexpected discovery—a bolt from the blue, as it were—you can always be sure that it has grown up by the influence of one man on another, and it is this mutual influence which makes the enormous possibility of scientific advance. Scientists are not dependent on the ideas of a single man, but on the combined wisdom of thousands of men, all thinking of the same problem, and each doing his little bit to add to the great structure of knowledge which is gradually being erected."

Shall we believe that Galileo less typifies the spirit of science than Rutherford?

Yet it was Galileo who, for the first time, showed how to resolve the complex motion of a projectile into two separate and different components—one uniform and the other accelerated—and it was Galileo who first put the scholastic laws of motion to the test of experiment and proved that they could be applied to the real world of experience. If it seems that this is only a small achievement, recall that the principles which Galileo made more precise and used as a part of physics rather than a part of logic had been known since the mid-fourteenth century, but that no one else in that 300-year interval had had the insight to see how to relate such abstractions to the world of nature. Perhaps in this we may best see the particular quality of his genius in combining the mathematical view of the world with the empirical view obtained by observation, critical experience, and true experiment.

Formulating the Law of Inertia

Let us explore a little further Galileo's contribution to scientific methodology in his insistence upon an exact relation between mathematical abstractions and the world of experience. For instance, most of the laws of motion as announced by Galileo would hold true only in a vacuum, where there would be no air resistance. But in the real world it is necessary to deal with the motions of bodies in various kinds of media, in which there is resistance. Hence, if the results Galileo obtained by the method of mathematical abstraction were to be applied to the real world around him, it was necessary for him to know exactly how much effect the resistance of the medium would have. In particular, Galileo was able to show that for bodies with some weight, and not designed to offer enormous resistances to motion through air, the effect of the air was almost negligible. It was this slight factor of air resistance that was responsible for the small difference in the times of descent of light and heavy objects from a given height. This difference was important, because it indicated that air has some resistance, but the smallness of the difference showed how minute the effect of this resistance actually is.

Galileo was able to demonstrate that a projectile follows the path of a parabola, because the projectile has simultaneously a combination of two independent motions: a uniform motion in a forward or horizontal direction, and a uniformly accelerated motion downward or in the vertical direction.

Commenting on this result, Galileo has Simplicio correctly argue, "I do not see how it is possible to avoid the resistance of the medium which must destroy the uni-

formity of the horizontal motion and change the law of
acceleration of falling bodies. These various difficulties
render it highly improbable that a result derived from
such unreliable hypotheses should hold true in practice."
The reply is then given, "I grant that these conclusions
proved in the abstract will be different when applied in
the concrete and will be fallacious to this extent, that
neither will the horizontal motion be uniform nor the
natural acceleration be in the ratio assumed, nor the
path of the projectile a parabola, etc." Galileo goes on
to prove, "In the case of those projectiles which we use,
made of dense material and round in shape, or of lighter
material and cylindrical in shape, such as arrows thrown
from a sling or crossbow, the deviation from an exact
parabolic path is quite insensible. Indeed, if you allow
me a little greater liberty, I can show you, by two experiments, that the dimensions of our apparatus are so
small that these external and incidental resistances,
among which that of the medium is the most considerable, are scarcely observable."

In one of the experiments Galileo used two balls, one
weighing ten or twelve times as much as the other, "one,
say, of lead, the other of oak, both allowed to fall from
an elevation of 150 or 200 cubits." According to Galileo, "Experiment shows that they will reach the earth
with slight difference in speed, showing us that in both
cases the retardation caused by the air is small; for if
both balls start at the same moment and at the same elevation, and if the leaden one be slightly retarded and the
wooden one greatly retarded, then the former ought to
reach the earth a considerable distance in advance of the
latter, since it is ten times as heavy. But this does not
happen; indeed, the gain in distance of one over the
other does not amount to the hundredth part of the entire fall. And in a case of a ball of stone weighing only
a third or half as much as one of lead, the difference

in their times of reaching the earth will be scarcely noticeable."

Next Galileo shows that, apart from weight, "the resistance of the air for a rapidly moving body is not very much greater than for one moving slowly." He assumed that "the resistance which the air offers to the motions studied by us . . . disturbs them all and disturbs them in an infinite variety of ways corresponding to the infinite variety in the form, weight, and velocity of the projectile" . . . "For as to velocity, the greater this is, the greater will be the resistance offered by the air; . . . So that although the falling body ought to be displaced in proportion to the square of the duration of its motion, yet no matter how heavy the body, if it falls from a very considerable height, the resistance of the air will be such as to prevent any increase in speed and will render the motion uniform; and in proportion as the moving body is less dense this uniformity will be so much the more quickly attained and after a shorter fall."

In this most interesting conclusion, Galileo says that if a body falls long enough, the resistance of the air will increase in some proportion to the speed until the resistance of the air equals and offsets the weight pulling the body down to the earth. If two bodies have the same size, and the same resistance because they have a similar shape, the heavier one will accelerate a longer time, because it has a greater weight. It will continue to accelerate until the resistance (proportional to the speed, which in turn is proportional to the time) equals the weight. What interests us is not this important result so much as Galileo's general conclusion: when the resistance becomes so great that it equals the weight of the falling body, the resistance of the air will "prevent any increase in speed and will render the motion uniform." This is to say that if the sum of all the forces acting upon a body (in this case the downward force of the weight and the upward force of the resistance) balance out or equal a net value

Fig. 20. *To see how Galileo analyzed projectile motion, consider a shell fired horizontally from a cannon at the edge of a cliff at a speed of 50 feet per second. The points, A, B, C, D show where the shell would be at the ends of successive seconds if there were no air-resistance and no downward component; in this case there being a uniform horizontal motion, the shell going 50 feet in each second. In the downward direction, there is an accelerated motion. The points a, b, c, d show where the shell would be if it were to fall with no air-resistance and no forward motion. Since the distance is computed by the law*

$$D = \tfrac{1}{2}AT^2$$

and the acceleration A is 32 ft/sec, the distances corresponding to these times are

T	T²	½AT²	D
1 sec	1 sec²	16 ft/sec² × 1 sec²	16 ft.
2 sec	4 sec²	16 ft/sec² × 4 sec²	64 ft.

of zero, the body will nevertheless continue to move, and will move uniformly. This is anti-Aristotelian, because Aristotle held that when the motive force equals the resistance the speed is zero. It is, in limited form, a statement of Newton's first law of motion, or the principle of inertia. According to this principle, the absence of an external force permits a body either to move in a straight line at constant speed or to stay at rest, and it thus sets up an equivalence between uniform rectilinear motion and rest, a principle that may be considered one of the major foundations of modern Newtonian physics.

But is Galileo's principle really the same as Newton's? Observe that in Galileo's statement there is not any reference to a general law of inertia, but only to the particular case of downward motion. This is a limited motion, because it can continue only until the falling object strikes the ground. There is no possibility, for example, of such a motion's continuing uniformly in a straight line forever, as may be inferred from Newton's more general statement.

3 sec	*9 sec²*	*16 ft/sec² × 9 sec²*	*144 ft.*
4 sec	*16 sec²*	*16 ft/sec² × 16 sec²*	*256 ft.*

Since the shell actually has the two motions simultaneously, the net path is as shown by the curve.

For those who like a bit of algebra, let v be the constant horizontal speed and x the horizontal distance, so that $x = vt$. *In the vertical direction let the distance be y, so that* $y = \frac{1}{2}At^2$. *Then,* $x^2 = v^2t^2$ *or*

$$\begin{cases} \dfrac{x^2}{v^2} = t^2 \\[2mm] \dfrac{2y}{A} = t^2 \end{cases}$$

and $\dfrac{x^2}{v^2} = \dfrac{2y}{A}$ *or* $y = \dfrac{A}{2v^2}x^2$ *which is of the form* $y = kx^2$

where k is a constant, and this is the classic equation of the parabola.

In the *Discourses and Demonstrations Concerning Two New Sciences"* Galileo approached the problem of inertia chiefly in relation to his study of the path of a projectile, which he wanted to show was a parabola (Fig. 20). Galileo considers a body sent out in a horizontal direction. It will then have two separate and independent motions. In the horizontal direction it will move with uniform velocity, except for the small slowing effect of air resistance. At the same time, its downward motion will be accelerated, just as a freely falling body is accelerated. It is the combination of these two motions that causes the trajectory to be parabolic. For his postulate that the downward component of the motion is the same as that of a freely falling body Galileo did not give an experimental proof, although he indicated the possibility of having one. He devised a little machine in which on an inclined plane (Fig. 21) a ball was projected horizontally, to move in a parabolic path.

Fig. 21. Galileo's simple apparatus for demonstrating projectile motion was a wedge. A ball started with horizontal motion at the top of the wedge falls toward the bottom of the inclined plane in a parabolic path.

Today we can easily demonstrate this conclusion by shooting one of a pair of balls horizontally, while the other is simultaneously allowed to fall freely from the same height. The result of such an experiment is shown in Plate VII, where a series of photographs taken stroboscopically at successive instants shows that although one of the balls is moving forward while the other is dropping vertically, the distances fallen in successive seconds are the same for both. This is the situation of a ball falling on a train moving at constant speed along a linear track. It falls *vertically* second after second just as it would if the train were at rest. Since it also moves horizontally at the same uniform speed as the train, its true path with respect to the earth is a parabola. Yet another modern example is that of an airplane flying horizontally at constant speed and releasing a bomb or torpedo. The downward fall is the same as if the bomb or torpedo had been dropped from the same height from an object at rest, say a captive balloon on a calm day. As the bomb or torpedo falls from the airplane, it will continue to move forward with the horizontal uniform speed of the airplane and will, except for the effects of the air, remain directly under the plane. But to an observer at rest on the earth, the trajectory will be a parabola.

Finally consider a stone dropped from a tower. With respect to the earth (and for such a short fall the movement of the earth can be considered linear and uniform), it falls straight downward. But with respect to the space determined by the fixed stars, it retains the motion shared with the earth at the moment of release, and its trajectory is therefore a parabola.

These analyses of parabolic trajectories are all based on the Galilean principle of separating a complex motion into two motions (or components) at right angles to each other. It is certainly a measure of his genius that he saw that a body could simultaneously have a uniform or nonaccelerated horizontal component of velocity and an accelerated vertical component—neither one in any way affecting the other. In every such case, the horizontal component exemplifies the tendency of a body that is moving at constant speed in a straight line to continue to do so, even though it loses physical contact with the original source of that uniform motion. This may also be described as a tendency of any body to resist any change in its state of motion, a property generally known since Newton's day as a body's inertia. Because inertia is so obviously important for understanding motion, we shall inquire a little more deeply into Galileo's views—not so much to show his limitations as to illustrate how difficult it was to formulate the full law of inertia and to overthrow the last vestiges of the old physics.

Galilean Difficulties and Achievements

Toward the end of Galileo's *Discourses and Demonstrations Concerning Two New Sciences* he introduces the subject of projectile motion as follows:

"Imagine any particle projected along a horizontal plane without friction; then we know . . . that this particle will move along this same plane with a motion which is uniform and perpetual, provided the plane has no limits."

But in Galileo's world of physics, can there be a "plane [which] has no limits"? In the real world, one certainly never finds such a plane.

In discussing motion along a plane Galileo admits the difficulties raised by Simplicio: "One of these [difficulties] is that we suppose the horizontal plane, which slopes neither up nor down, to be represented by a straight line as if each point on this line were equally distant from the center, which is not the case; for as one starts from the middle [of the line] and goes toward either end, he departs farther and farther from the center [of the earth] and is therefore constantly going uphill." Thus if it is moving along any considerable plane tangent to the surface of the earth, a ball will begin to go up hill, which would destroy the uniformity of its motion. But in the real world of experiments, things are different, for then, Galileo states, "Our instruments and the distances involved are so small in comparison with the enormous distance from the center of the earth that we may consider a minute of arc on a great circle as a

Plate V. "In fair and grateful exchange," as Galileo put it, the earth contributes illumination to the moon. This photograph, taken at Yerkes Observatory, shows earthshine on the portion of the moon that otherwise would be in shadow.

Plate VI. A ball fired with a spring gun in the smokestack of a moving toy locomotive describes a parabola and lands in the smokestack of going straight up and down as it does when the locomotive is standing still. These stroboscopic pictures, with exposures at intervals of one-thirtieth of a second, vividly illustrate one of Galileo's arguments on the behavior of falling bodies and settle the ancient debate about bodies dropped from the masts of moving ships. If the speed of the locomotive were absolutely uniform and if the ball met no air resistance, it would land in the smokestack. (In fact, even under the imperfect conditions of the experiment, the ball hits the smokestack more often than not.) Note that the ball attains the same height whether the locomotive is at rest or moving. Notice, too, that in the picture where the locomotive is standing still, the distances traveled by the ball in the intervals of exposure correspond almost exactly. On the ascent, gravity

Plate VII. The independence of the vertical and horizontal components of projectile motion is illustrated in this stroboscopic photograph. In intervals of one-thirtieth of a second the projected ball falling along a parabolic path drops exactly the same distance as the ball allowed to fall vertically. Photograph by Berenice Abbott.

NEWTON

KEPLER · · · · · GALILEO

Plate VIII.

straight line. . . ." Galileo explains what considering an arc a straight line will mean: "Archimedes and the others considered themselves as located at an infinite distance from the center of the earth, in which case their assumptions were not false, and therefore their conclusions were absolutely correct. When we wish to apply our proven conclusions to distances which, though finite, are very large, it is necessary for us to infer, on the basis of demonstrated truth, what correction is to be made for the fact that our distance from the center of the earth is not really infinite, but merely very great in comparison with the small dimensions of our apparatus." As in his discussion of air resistance, Galileo here wants to know just what the effect may be of a factor which he wishes to ignore. How much error arises from considering a small portion of the earth to be a plane? Very little for most problems.

Earlier, in presenting Galileo's thought on terminal velocities, we called attention to his view that the air resistance increases as some function of the speed. Hence, after falling for some time, a body may generate an air resistance equal to its weight, and then undergo no further acceleration. Under a zero net external force, the body will move in a straight line at constant speed. This is a clear illustration of how a vertical downward motion toward the earth may exemplify a principle of inertia. The projectile seemed, likewise, to exemplify the principle of inertia in its horizontal movement, the component of velocity along the earth. But now we are told that if horizontal motion means motion along a plane tangent to the earth, this motion cannot truly be inertial since in any direction away from the point of tangency the body, though still moving along the plane, will be going uphill! Evidently, we must accept the conclusion that if such a motion is to be inertial and continue at constant speed *without an external force,* the "plane" on which the body is moving is not a true geometric plane at all but a portion of the earth's surface, which can be taken as planar only because of the relatively large radius of the earth. For Galileo, it would seem the principle of inertia applied to objects moving downward along straight line segments terminating at the earth's surface and along the earth's surface itself. The latter motion not being truly along a straight line, Galileo's concept is sometimes referred to as a kind of "circular inertia."

For enlightenment on Galileo's point of view, we may turn to his *Dialogue Concerning the Two Chief World Systems.* In this work he writes unambiguously of inertia as a circular rather than a linear principle. Here—as in the *Two New Sciences*—he discusses a motion compounded of two separate and independent movements; uniform motion in a circle and accelerated motion in a straight line toward the center of the earth. The reason that Galileo thought in terms of a circular inertia appears to be a desire to explain how on a rotating earth a falling body will always continue to fall downward just as if the earth were at rest. Evidently the straight downward falling of a weight on a rotating earth implied to Galileo that the falling weight must continue to rotate with the earth. Thus he conceived that a ball falling from a tower would continue to move through equal circular arcs in equal times (as any point on the earth does) while nevertheless descending according to the law of uniformly accelerated bodies toward the center of the earth.

There is one place in the *Dialogue* when it almost appears that Galileo has hit upon the principle of inertia. Salviati asks Simplicio what would happen to a ball placed on a downward sloping plane. Simplicio agrees that it would accelerate spontaneously. Similarly, on an upward slope, a force would be needed to "thrust it along or even to hold it still." What would happen if such a body were "placed upon a surface with no slope upward or downward?" Simplicio says there would be neither a "natural tendency toward motion" nor a "resistance to being moved." Hence, the object would remain stationary, or at rest. Salviati agrees that this is what would happen if the ball were laid down gently, but if it were given a push directing it toward any part, what would happen? Simplicio replies that it would move in that direction, and that there would not be "cause for acceleration or deceleration, there being no slope upward or downward." There is no cause for "the ball's retardation," nor "for its coming to rest." Salviati then asks how far the ball would continue to move in these circumstances. The reply is, "as far as the extension of the surface continued without rising or falling." Next, Salviati says, "Then if such a space were unbounded, the motion on it would likewise be boundless, that is, would be perpetual." To which Simplicio agrees.

At this point it might seem that Galileo has postulated the modern form of the principle of inertia, in which a body projected on an infinite plane would continue to move uniformly forever. And this is emphasized when Simplicio says that the motion would be "perpetual" if "the body is of a durable matter." But Salviati then asks him what he thinks is "the cause of the ball moving spontaneously on the downward inclined plane, but only by force on the one tilted upward?" Simplicio replies that "The tendency of heavy bodies is to move toward the center of the earth, and to move upward from its circumference only with force" being put into violent motion. Salviati then says, "Then in order for a surface to be [sloping] neither downward nor upward, all its parts must be equally distant from the center. Are there any such surfaces in the world?" Simplicio replies, "Plenty of them; such would be the surface of our terrestrial globe if it were smooth, and not rough and mountainous as it is. But there is that of water, when it is placid and tranquil." Salviati next says that then "a ship, when it moves over a calm sea, is one of these movables which courses over a surface that is tilted neither up nor down, and if all external and accidental obstacles were removed, it would thus be disposed to move incessantly and uniformly from an impulse once received?" Simplicio agrees, "It seems that it ought to be [so]."

Clearly, then, what has seemed at first to be an infinite plane has shrunk in the discussion to a segment of the spherical surface of the earth. And that motion which was said to be "perpetual," and appeared to be uniform motion along an infinite plane, has turned out to be a ship moving on a calm sea, or any other object that moves along a smooth sphere like the earth. And it is precisely this point which Galileo wished to prove, because he now can explain that a stone let fall from a ship will continue to move around the earth as the ship moves, and so will fall from the top of the mast to the foot of the mast. "Now as to that stone which is on top of the mast. Does it not move, carried by the ship, both of them going along the circumference of the circle about its center? And consequently is there not in it an ineradicable motion, all external impediments being removed? And is not this motion as fast as that of the ship?" Simplicio is allowed to draw his own conclusion: "You mean that the stone, moving with an indelibly impressed motion, is not going to leave the [moving] ship, but will follow it, and finally will fall at the same place where it fell when the ship remained motionless."

One of the reasons why Galileo would have found the principle of inertia in its Newtonian form objectionable is that it implies an infinite universe. The Newtonian principle of inertia says that a body moving without the action of any forces will continue to move forever in a straight line at constant speed, and if it moves forever at a constant speed, it must have the potentiality of moving through a space which is unbounded and unlimited. But Galileo states in his discussion of the *Two Systems*

of the World that "Every body constituted in a state of
rest but naturally capable of motion will move when set
at liberty only if it has a natural tendency toward some
particular place." Hence, a body cannot simply move
away from a place, but only *toward* a place. He also
states unequivocally, "Besides, straight motion being by
nature infinite (because a straight line is infinite and in-
determinate), it is impossible that anything should have
by nature the principle of moving in a straight line; or, in
other words, toward a place where it is impossible to
arrive, there being no finite end. For nature, as Aristotle
well says himself, never undertakes to do that which cannot be done, nor endeavors to move whither it is impossible to arrive." It is thus apparent that when Galileo talks about rectilinear motion, he means motion
along a limited portion of a straight line or, as we would
put it technically, along a straight line segment. For
Galileo, as for his medieval predecessors, motion still
means "local motion," a translation from one place to
another, a motion to a fixed destination and not a motion that merely continues in some specified direction
forever—save for circular motions.

Galileo's first published reference to a kind of inertia
appears in his famous *History and Demonstrations Concerning Sunspots and Their Phenomena,* published in
Rome in 1613, four years after he began his observations with the telescope. In talking about the rotation
of the spots around the sun, he set forth a principle of
"circular inertia," holding that an object set on a circular
path will continue in that path at constant speed along
a circle forever, unless there is the action of an external
force. Here is what he says:

> "For I seem to have observed that physical bodies
> have physical inclination to some motion (as heavy
> bodies downward), which motion is exercised by
> them through an intrinsic property and without need

of a particular external mover, whenever they are not impeded by some obstacle. And to another motion they have a repugnance (as the same heavy bodies to motion upward), and therefore they never move in that manner unless thrown violently by an external mover.

"Finally, to some movements they are indifferent, as are these same heavy bodies to horizontal motion, to which they have neither inclination (since it is not toward the center of the earth) nor repugnance (since it does not carry them away from that center). And therefore all external impediments removed, a heavy body on a spherical surface concentric with the earth will be indifferent to rest and to movements toward any part of the horizon. And it will maintain itself in that state in which it has once been placed; that is, if placed in a state of rest, it will conserve that; and if placed in movement toward the west (for example) it will maintain itself in that movement. Thus a ship, for instance, having once received some impetus through the tranquil sea, would move continually around our globe without ever stopping; and placed at rest it would perpetually remain at rest, if in the first case all extrinsic impediments could be removed, and in the second case no external cause of motion were added."

Galileo's limitation on circular inertia was attributed, a few paragraphs ago, to a wish to avoid the consequences of an infinite universe, and also to a need to explain why a body falls vertically on a rotating earth. But the problem is made more complicated by the fact that Galileo was undoubtedly acting in accordance with the general ideas of his time, in which a special place was given to circular motions. This was true not only in the Aristotelian physics but also in the Copernican approach to the universe. Copernicus, echoing a neo-Platonic idea, had said that the universe is spherical "either because that figure is the most perfect . . . or because it is the most capacious [i.e., of all possible solids, a sphere has the largest volume for a given surface area] and therefore best suited for that which is to contain and preserve all things; or again because all the perfect parts of it, namely, sun, moon and stars, are so formed; or because all things tend to assume this shape, as is seen in the case of drops of water and liquid bodies in general if freely formed." Since the earth is spherical, Copernicus asked, "Why then hesitate to grant earth that power of motion natural to its [spherical] shape, rather than suppose a gliding round of the whole universe, whose limits are unknown and unknowable." Galileo echoed such ideas about circles in his advocacy of the Copernican system.

If Galileo is seen to be a creature of his time, still caught up in the principles of circularity in physics, we may observe the extent to which the general thought patterns of an age can limit men of the greatest genius. And the consequences, in the case of Galileo, are particularly interesting in the context of the present book. We shall call attention to two of them, which will be discussed in the next chapter. First of all, Galileo's attachment to circles for planetary orbits prevented him from accepting the concept of elliptical planetary orbits, the outstanding discovery of his contemporary Kepler, published in 1609 just as Galileo was pointing the telescope heavenwards. Secondly, since Galileo restricted the principle of inertia as he conceived it to rotating bodies and to heavy bodies moving freely upon smooth spheres with the same center as the earth (with the exception of terrestrial objects moving on limited straight line segments), he never achieved a true celestial mechanics. Apparently he did not try to explain the orbital motion of the planets by means of any kind of circularly acting inertial principle, and, as Stillman Drake, the lead-ing American Galileo expert, has well said, Galileo "did not attempt any explanation of the cause of planetary motions, except to imply that if the nature of gravity were known this too might be discovered." This was an achievement reserved for Newton.

We shall see that Newton established an inertial physics that provides a dynamics of celestial bodies as well as of terrestrial objects and in which there is only *linear inertia* and no circular inertia at all. No small part of Newton's genius, in fact, is exhibited in his analysis of circular motion, proving that there is an inertial component *in the linear sense* combined with a continual falling away from the straight line to the circular path. Hence, unlike Galileo, Newton showed that motion along a circle is non-inertial; thus it requires a force. In uniform circular motion Newton and his contemporary Christian Huygens showed that there is an acceleration which is nonuniform, and so of a sort that lay beyond Galileo's ken.

Some scholars have seen the whole of Galileo's scientific career as exemplifying his battle for the Copernican system. Certainly his war against Aristotle and Ptolemy was intended to destroy both the concept of a geostatic universe and the physics based upon it. The telescope enabled him to shake the foundations of Ptolemaic astronomy, and his investigations in dynamics led him to a new viewpoint from which events on a moving earth would have the same appearance as on a stationary earth. Galileo did not really explain how the earth could move, but he was successful in showing why terrestrial experiments such as the dropping of weights can neither prove nor disprove the motion of the earth.

The unity of Galileo's scientific life, combining observational astronomy and mathematical physics, comes from his dedication to a sun-centered universe—a dedication reinforced in some way by every major discovery he made in either physics or astronomy. Having been the instrument by which the glorious aspects of the creation in the heavens first had been fully revealed to a mortal, Galileo must have had a special sense of urgency to convert all his fellow men to the true—that is, the Copernican—system of the universe. His conflict with the Roman Catholic Church arose because deep in his heart Galileo was a true believer. There was for him no path of compromise, no way to have separate secular and theological cosmologies. If the Copernican system was true as he believed, then what else could Galileo do but fight with every weapon in his arsenal of logic, rhetoric, scientific observation, mathematical theory, and cunning insight, to make his Church accept a new system of the universe? Alas for Galileo, the time was wrong for the Church to make this change, or so it seemed then, following the Council of Trent and its insistence on the literal interpretation of Scripture. There was no avoiding conflict, and the consequences still echo around us in a never-ending literature of controversy. In the contrast between Galileo's heroic stand when he tried to reform the cosmological basis of orthodox theology and his humbled, kneeling surrender when he disavowed his Copernicanism, we may sense the tremendous forces attendant on the birth of modern science. And we may catch a glimpse of the spirit of this great man as we think of him, after his trial and condemnation, living under a kind of house-arrest or surveillance as Milton saw him in *Arcetri*, completing his greatest scientific work, *Discourses and Demonstrations Concerning Two New Sciences*. This book was the base from which Newton began his great exploration of the dynamical principles of a sun-centered universe.

CHAPTER 6

Kepler's Celestial Music

Since Greek times scientists have insisted that Nature is simple. A familiar maxim of Aristotle is, "Nature does nothing in vain, nothing superfluous." Another expression of this philosophy has come down to us from a fourteenth-century English monk and scholar, William of Occam. Known as his "law of parsimony" or "Occam's razor" (perhaps for its ruthless cutting away of the superfluous), it maintains, "Entities are not to be multiplied without necessity." "It is vain to do with more what can be done with fewer" perhaps sums up this attitude.

We have seen Galileo assume a principle of simplicity in his approach to the problem of accelerated motion, and the literature of modern physical science suggests countless other examples. Indeed, present-day physics is in distress, or at least in an uneasy state, because the recently discovered nuclear "fundamental particles" exhibit a stubborn disinclination to recognize simple laws. Only a few decades ago physicists complacently assumed that the proton and the electron were the only "fundamental particles" they needed to explain the atom. But now one "fundamental particle" after another has crept into the ranks until it appears that there may be as many of them as there are chemical elements. Confronted with this bewildering array, the average physicist is tempted to echo Alfonso the Wise and bemoan the fact that he was not consulted first.

Anyone who examines Fig. 14 on page 58 will see at

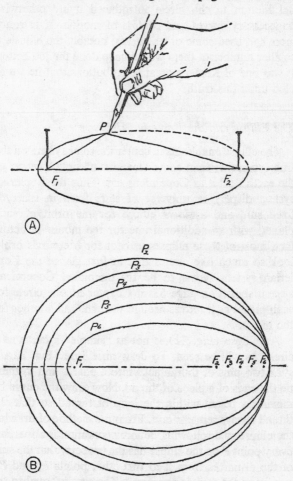

Fig. 22. The ellipse, drawn in the manner shown in (A), can have all the shapes shown in (B) if you use the same string but vary the distance between the pins, as at F_2, F_3, F_4, etc.

once that neither the Ptolemaic nor Copernican system was, in any sense of the word, "simple." Today we know why these systems lacked simplicity: restricting celestial motion to the circle introduced many otherwise unnecessary curves and centers of motion. If astronomers had used some other curves, notably the ellipse, a smaller number of them would have done the job better. It was one of Kepler's great contributions that he stumbled upon this truth.

The Ellipse and the Keplerian Universe

The ellipse enables us to center the solar system on the true sun rather than some "mean sun" or the center of the earth's orbit as Copernicus did. Thus the Keplerian system displays a universe of stars fixed in space, a fixed sun, and a *single* ellipse for the orbit of each planet, with an additional one for the moon. In actual fact, most of these ellipses, except for Mercury's orbit, look so much like circles that at first glance the Keplerian system seems to be the simplified Copernican system shown on page 58 of Chapter 3: one circle for each planet as it moves around the sun, and another for the moon.

An ellipse (Fig. 22) is not as "simple" a curve as a circle, as will be seen. To draw an ellipse (Fig. 22A), stick two pins or thumbtacks into a board, and to them tie the ends of a piece of thread. Now draw the curve by moving a pencil within the loop of thread so that the thread always remains taut. From the method of drawing the ellipse, the following defining condition is apparent: every point P on the ellipse has the property that the sum of the distances from it to two other points F_1 and F_2, known as the *foci*, is constant. (The sum is equal to the length of the string.) For any pair of foci, the chosen length of the string determines the size and shape of the ellipse, which may also be varied by using one string-length and placing the pins near to, or far from, one another. Thus an ellipse may have a shape (Fig. 22B) with more or less the proportions of an egg, a cigar, or a needle, or may be almost round and like a circle. But unlike the true egg, cigar, or needle, the ellipse must always be symmetrical (Fig. 23) with respect to the axes,

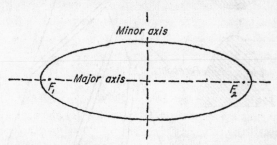

Fig. 23. The ellipse is always symmetrical with respect to its major and minor axes.

one of which (the major axis) is a line drawn across the ellipse through the foci and the other (the minor axis) a line drawn across the ellipse along the perpendicular bisector of the major axis. If the two foci are allowed to coincide, the ellipse becomes a circle; another way of saying this is that the circle is a "degenerate" form of an ellipse.

The properties of the ellipse were described in antiquity by Apollonius of Perga, the Greek geometer who inaugurated the scheme of epicycles used in Ptolemaic astronomy. Apollonius showed that the ellipse, the parabola (the path of a projectile according to Galilean mechanics), the circle, and another curve called the hyperbola may be formed (Fig. 24) by passing planes at different inclinations through a right cone, or a cone of revolution. But until the time of Kepler and Galileo, no one had ever shown that the conic sections occur in natural phenomena, notably in the phenomena of motion.

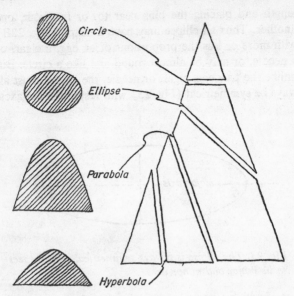

Fig. 24. The conic sections are obtained by cutting a cone in ways shown. Note that the circle is cut parallel to the base of the cone, the parabola parallel to one side.

In this work we shall not discuss the stages whereby Johannes Kepler came to make his discoveries. Not that the subject is devoid of interest. Far from it! But at present we are concerned with the rise of a new physics, as it was related to the writings of antiquity, the Middle Ages, the Renaissance and the seventeenth century. Aristotle's books were read widely, and so were the writings of Galileo and Newton. Men studied Ptolemy's *Almagest* and Copernicus's *De revolutionibus* carefully. But Kepler's writings were not so generally read. Newton, for example, knew the works of Galileo but he probably did not read Kepler's books. He may even have acquired his knowledge of Kepler's laws at secondhand, very likely from Seth Ward's textbook on astronomy. Even today there is no major work of Kepler available in a complete English, French, or Italian translation!

This neglect of Kepler's texts is not hard to understand. The language and style were of unimaginable difficulty and prolixity, which, in contrast with the clarity and vigor of Galileo's every word, seemed formidable beyond endurance. This is to be expected, for writing reflects the personality of the author. Kepler was a tortured mystic, who stumbled onto his great discoveries in a weird groping that has led his most recent biographer,* to call him a "sleepwalker." Trying to prove one thing, he discovered another, and in his calculations he made error after error that canceled each other out. He was utterly unlike Galileo and Newton; never could their purposeful quests for truth conceivably merit the description of sleepwalking. Kepler, who wrote sketches of himself in the third person, said that he became a Copernican as a student and that "There were three things in particular, namely, the number, distances and motions of the heavenly bodies, as to which I [Kepler] searched zealously for reasons why they were as they were and not otherwise." About the sun-centered system of Copernicus, Kepler at another time wrote: "I certainly know that I owe it this duty: that since I have attested it as true in my deepest soul, and since I contemplate its beauty with incredible and ravishing delight, I should also publicly defend it to my readers with all the force at my command." But it was not enough to defend the system; he set out to devote his whole life to finding a law or set of laws that would show how the system held together, why the planets had the particular orbits in which they are found, and why they move as they do.

The first installment in this program, published in 1596, when Kepler was twenty-five years old, was en-

* Arthur Koestler, *The Sleepwalkers*, Hutchinson & Co., London, 1959.

titled *Forerunner of the Dissertations on the Universe, containing the Mystery of the Universe.* In this book Kepler announced what he considered a great discovery concerning the distances of the planets from the sun. This discovery shows us how rooted Kepler was in the Platonic-Pythagorean tradition, how he sought to find regularities in nature associated with the regularities of mathematics. The Greek geometers had discovered that there are five "regular solids," which are shown in Fig. 25. In the Copernican system there are six planets:

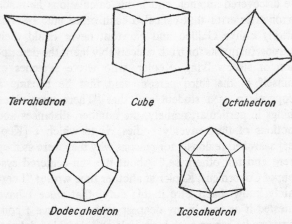

Fig. 25. "Regular" polygons. The tetrahedron has four faces, each an equilateral triangle. The cube has six faces, each a square. The octahedron has eight faces, each an equilateral triangle. Each of the dodecahedron's twelve faces is an equilateral pentagon. The twenty faces of the icosahedron are all equilateral triangles.

Mercury, Venus, Earth, Mars, Jupiter, Saturn. Hence it occurred to Kepler that five regular solids might separate six planetary orbits.

He started with the simplest of these solids, the cube.

A cube can be circumscribed by one and only one sphere, just as one and only one sphere can be inscribed in a cube. Hence we may have a cube that is circumscribed by sphere No. 1 and contains sphere No. 2. This sphere No. 2 just contains the next regular solid, the tetrahedron, which in turn contains sphere No. 3. This sphere No. 3 contains the dodecahedron, which in turn contains sphere No. 4. Now it happens that in this scheme the radii of the successive spheres are in more or less the same proportion as the mean distances of the planets in the Copernican system except for Jupiter—which isn't surprising, said Kepler, considering how far Jupiter is from the sun. The first Keplerian scheme (Fig. 26), then, was this:

> Sphere of Saturn
> *Cube*
> Sphere of Jupiter
> *Tetrahedron*
> Sphere of Mars
> *Dodecahedron*
> Sphere of Earth
> *Icosahedron*
> Sphere of Venus
> *Octahedron*
> Sphere of Mercury.

"I undertake," he said, "to prove that God, in creating the universe and regulating the order of the cosmos, had in view the five regular bodies of geometry as known since the days of Pythagoras and Plato, and that He has fixed, according to those dimensions, the number of heavens, their proportions, and the relations of their movements." Even though this book fell short of unqualified success, it established Kepler's reputation as a clever mathematician and as a man who really knew something about astronomy. On the basis of this performance, Tycho Brahe offered him a job.

Fig. 26. Kepler's model of the universe. This weird contraption, consisting of the five regular solids fitted together, was dearer to his heart than the three laws on which his fame rests. From Christophorus Leibfried (1597).

Tycho Brahe (1546–1601) has been said to have been the reformer of astronomical observation. Using huge and well-constructed instruments, he had so increased the accuracy of naked-eye determinations of planetary positions and of the locations of the stars relative to one another that it was clear that neither the system of Ptolemy nor that of Copernicus would truly predict the celestial appearances. Furthermore, in contrast to earlier astronomers, Tycho did not merely observe the planets now and then to provide factors for a theory or to check such a theory; instead he observed a planet whenever it was visible, night after night. When Kepler eventually became Tycho's successor, he inherited the largest and most accurate collection of planetary observations—notably for the planet Mars—that had ever been assembled. Tycho, it may be recalled, believed in neither the Ptolemaic nor the Copernican system but had advanced a geocentric system of his own devising. Kepler, faithful to a promise he had made to Tycho, tried to fit Tycho's data on the planet Mars into the Tychonian system. He failed as he failed also to fit the data into the Copernican system. But twenty-five years of labor did produce a new and improved theory of the solar system.

Kepler presented his first major results in a work entitled *Commentaries on the Motions of Mars,* published in 1609, the year in which Galileo first pointed his telescope skyward. Kepler had made seventy different trials of putting the data obtained by Tycho into the Copernican epicycles and the Tychonian circles but always failed. Evidently it was necessary to give up all the accepted methods of computing planetary orbits or to reject Tycho's observations as being inaccurate. Kepler's failure may not appear as miserable as he seemed to think. After calculating eccentrics, epicycles, and equants in ingenious combinations, he was able to obtain an agreement between theoretical predictions and the observations of Tycho that was off by only 8 minutes (8′) of angle. Copernicus himself had never hoped to attain an accuracy greater than 10′, and the *Prussian Tables,* computed by Reinhold on the basis of Copernican methods, were off by as much as 5°. In 1609, before the application of telescopes to astronomy, 8′ was not a large angle; 8′ is just twice the minimum separation the unaided average eye can distinguish between two stars.

But Kepler was not to be satisfied by any approximation. He believed in the Copernican sun-centered system and he also believed in the accuracy of Tycho's observations. Thus, he wrote:

> "Since the divine goodness has given to us in Tycho Brahe a most careful observer, from whose observations the error of 8′ is shewn in this calculation . . . it is right that we should with gratitude recognise and make use of this gift of God. . . . For if I could have treated 8′ of longitude as negligible I should have already corrected sufficiently the hypothesis . . . discovered in chapter xvi. But as they could not be neglected, these 8′ alone have led the way towards the complete reformation of astronomy, and have been made the subject-matter of a great part of this work."

Starting afresh, Kepler finally took the revolutionary step of rejecting circles altogether, trying an egg-shaped oval curve and eventually the ellipse. To appreciate how revolutionary this step actually was, recall that both Aristotle and Plato had insisted that planetary orbits had to be combined out of circles, and that this principle was a feature common to both Ptolemy's *Almagest* and Copernicus's *De revolutionibus.* Galileo, Kepler's friend, politely ignored the strange aberration. But the final victory was Kepler's. He not only got rid of innumerable circles, requiring but one oval curve per planet, but he made the system accurate and found a wholly new and unsuspected relation between the location of a planet and its orbital speed.

The Three Laws

Kepler's problem was not only to determine the orbit of Mars, but at the same time to find the orbit of the earth. The reason is that our observations of Mars are made from the earth, which itself does not move uniformly in a perfect circle in the Copernican system. Fortunately, however, the earth's orbit is almost circular. Kepler discarded Copernicus's idea that all planetary orbits should be centered on the mid-point of the earth's orbit. He stated, instead, that *the orbit of each planet is in the shape of an ellipse with the sun located at one focus.* This principle is known as Kepler's first law.

Kepler's second law tells us about the speed with which a planet moves in its orbit. This law states that *in any equal time intervals, a line from the planet to the sun will sweep out equal areas.* Fig. 27 shows equal areas for three regions in a planetary orbit. Since the three

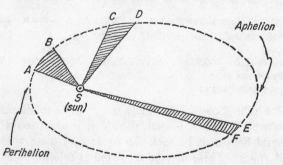

Fig. 27. Kepler's law of equal areas. Since a planet moves through the arcs ĀB̄, C̄D̄ and ĒF̄ in equal times (because the areas SAB, SCD, and SEF are equal), it travels fastest at perihelion, when nearest the sun, and slowest at aphelion, when farthest from the sun. The shape of this ellipse is that of a comet's orbit. Planetary ellipses are more nearly circular.

shaded regions are of equal area, the planet moves most quickly when nearest to the sun and most slowly when farthest from the sun. This second law thus tells us at once that the apparent irregularity in the speed with which planets move in their orbits is a variation obeying a simple geometric condition.

The first and second law plainly show how Kepler simplified the Copernican system. But the third law, known also as the harmonic law, is even more interesting. It is called the harmonic law because its discoverer thought it demonstrated the true celestial harmonies. Kepler even entitled the book in which he announced it *The Harmony of the World* (1619). The third law states a relation between the periodic times in which the planets complete their orbits about the sun and their average distances from the sun. Let us make a table of the periodic times (T) and average distances (D). In this table and in the following text, the distances are given in astronomical units. One astronomical unit is, by definition, the mean distance from the earth to the sun.

	Mercury	Venus	Earth	Mars	Jupiter	Saturn
periodic time T (years)	0.24	0.615	1.00	1.88	11.68	29.457
mean distance from the sun D (astronomical units)	0.387	0.723	1.00	1.524	5.203	9.539

This table shows us that there is no simple relationship between D and T. Kepler, therefore, tried to see what would happen if he took the squares of these values, D^2 and T^2. These may be tabulated as follows:

	Mercury	Venus	Earth	Mars	Jupiter	Saturn
T^2	0.058	0.38	1.00	3.54	140	868
D^2	0.147	0.528	1.00	2.323	27.071	90.792

There is still no relation discernible between D and T^2, or between D^2 and T, or even between D^2 and T^2. Any ordinary mortal would have given up at this point. Not

Kepler. He was so convinced that these numbers must be related that he would never have given up. The next power is the cube. T^3 turns out to be of no use, but D^3 yields the following numbers. Note them and then turn back to the table of squares.

	Mercury	Venus	Earth	Mars	Jupiter	Saturn
D^3	0.058	0.38	1.00	3.54	140	868

Here then are the celestial harmonies, the third law, which states that the *squares of times of revolution of any two planets around the sun* (earth included) *are proportional to the cubes of their mean distances from the sun.*

In mathematical language, we may say that "T^2 is always proportional to D^3" or

$$\frac{D^3}{T^2} = K,$$

where K is a constant. If we choose as units for D and T the astronomical unit and the year, then K has the numerical value of unity. (But if the distance were measured in miles and time in seconds, the value of the constant K is not unity.) Another way of expressing Kepler's third law is

$$\frac{D_1^3}{T_1^2} = \frac{D_2^3}{T_2^2} = \frac{D_3^3}{T_3^2} = \frac{D_4^3}{T_4^2} = \ldots \ldots = K$$

where D_1 and T_1, D_2 and T_2, . . . , are the respective distances and periods of any planet in the solar system.

To see how this law may be applied, let us suppose that a new planet were discovered at a mean distance of $4AU$ from the sun. What is its period of revolution? Kepler's third law tells us that the ratio D^3/T^2 for this new planet must be the same as the ratio D_0^3/T_0^2 for the earth. That is,

$$\frac{D^3}{T^2} = \frac{(1AU)^3}{(1^y)^2}.$$

Since $D = 4AU$,

$$\frac{(4AU)^3}{T^2} = \frac{(1AU)^3}{(1^y)^2},$$

$$\frac{64}{T^2} = \frac{1}{(1^y)^2}$$

$$T^2 = 64 \times (1^y)^2$$

$$T = 8^y.$$

The inverse problem may also be solved. What is the distance from the sun of a planet having a period of 125 years?

$$\frac{D^3}{T^2} = \frac{(1AU)^3}{(1^y)^2}$$

$$\frac{D^3}{(125^y)^2} = \frac{(1AU)^3}{(1^y)^2}$$

$$\frac{D^3}{125 \times 125} = \frac{(1AU)^3}{1}$$

$$D^3 = 25 \times 25 \times 25 \times (1AU)^3$$

$$D = 25AU.$$

Similar problems can be solved for any satellite system. The significance of this third law is that it is a law of necessity; that is, it states that it is impossible in any satellite system for satellites to move at just any speed or at any distance. Once the distance is chosen, the speed is determined. In our solar system this law implies that the sun provides the governing force that keeps the planets moving as they do. In no other way can we account for the fact that the speed is so precisely related to distance from the sun. Kepler thought that the action of the sun was, in part at least, magnetic. It was known in his day that a magnet attracts another magnet even though considerable distances separate them. The motion of one magnet produces motion in another. Kepler was aware that a physician of Queen Elizabeth, William Gilbert (1544–1603), had shown the earth to be a huge magnet.

If all objects in the solar system are alike rather than different, as Galileo had shown and as the heliocentric system implied, why should not the sun and the other planets also be magnets like the earth?

Kepler's supposition, however tempting, does not lead directly to an explanation of why planets move in ellipses and sweep out equal areas in equal times. Nor does it tell us why the particular distance-period relation he found actually holds. Nor does it seem in any way related to such problems as the downward fall of bodies —according to the Galilean law of fall—on a stationary or on a moving earth, since the average rock or piece of wood is not magnetic. And yet we shall see that Newton, who eventually answered all these questions, based his discoveries on the laws found by Kepler and Galileo.

Kepler versus the Copernicans

Why were Kepler's beautiful results not universally accepted by Copernicans? Between the time of their publication (I, II, 1609; III, 1619) and the publication of Newton's *Principia* in 1687, there are very few references to Kepler's laws. Galileo, who had received copies of Kepler's books and who was certainly aware of the proposal of elliptic orbits, never referred in his scientific writings to any of the laws of Kepler, either to praise or to criticize them. In part, Galileo's reaction must have been Copernican, to stick to the belief in true circularity, implied in the very title of Copernicus's book: *On the Revolution of the Celestial Spheres*. That work opened with a theorem: 1. *That the Universe is Spherical*. Copernicus's arguments were given at the end of the last chapter. This is followed by a discussion of the topic, "That the motion of the heavenly bodies is uniform, circular, and perpetual, or composed of circular motions." The main line here is:

"Rotation is natural to a sphere and by that very act is its shape expressed. For here we deal with the simplest kind of body, wherein neither beginning nor end may be discerned nor, if it rotates ever in the same place, may the one be distinguished from the other.

"We must conclude [despite any observed apparent irregularities, such as the retrogradations of planets] that the motions of these bodies are ever circular or compounded of circles. For the irregularities themselves are subject to a definite law and recur at stated times, and this could not happen if the motions were not circular, for a circle alone can thus restore the place of a body as it was. So with the Sun which, by a compounding of circular motions, brings ever again the changing days and nights and the four seasons of the year."

Kepler thus was acting in a most un-Copernican way by not assuming that the planetary orbits are neither "circles" nor "compounded of circles"; furthermore he had come to his conclusion in part by reintroducing the one aspect of Ptolemaic astronomy to which Copernicus had most objected, the equant. Kepler said that a line from any planet to the empty focus of its ellipse (Fig. 28) rotates uniformly, or that such a line would rotate through equal angles in equal times because that other focus is the *equant*. (Incidentally, we may observe that this latter "discovery" of Kepler's is not true.)

From every point of view, the ellipses must have seemed objectionable. What kind of force could steer a planet along an elliptical path with just the proper variation of speed demanded by the law of equal areas? We shall not reproduce Kepler's discussion of this point, but shall confine our attention to one aspect of it. Kepler supposed that some kind of force or emanation comes out of the sun and moves the planets. This force—it is sometimes called an *anima motrix*—does not spread out

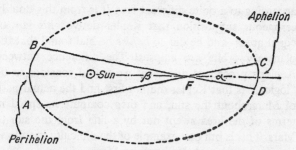

Fig. 28. Kepler's law of the equant. If a planet moves so that in equal times it sweeps out equal angles with respect to the empty focus at F, it will move through arcs $\overarc{AB}$ and $\overarc{CD}$ in the same time because the angles α and β are equal. According to this law, the planet moves faster along arc $\overarc{AB}$ (at perihelion) than along arc $\overarc{CD}$ (at aphelion) as the law of equal areas predicts. Nevertheless, this law is false.

in all directions from the sun. Why should it? After all, its function is only to move the planets, and the planets all lie in, or very nearly in, a single plane, the plane of the ecliptic. Hence Kepler supposed that this *anima motrix* spread out only in the plane of the ecliptic. Kepler had discovered that light, which spreads in all directions from a luminous source, diminishes in its intensity as the inverse square of the distance; that is, if there is a certain intensity or brightness three feet away from a lamp, the brightness six feet away will be one-fourth as great because four is the square of two and the new distance is twice the old. In equation form,

$$\text{intensity} \propto \frac{1}{(\text{distance})^2}$$

But Kepler held that the solar force does not spread out in all directions according to the inverse-square law, as the solar light does, but only in the plane of the ecliptic according to a quite different law. It is from this doubly erroneous supposition that Kepler derived his law of equal areas—and he did so *before* he had found that the planetary orbits are ellipses! The difference between Kepler's procedure and what we would consider to be "logical" is that Kepler did *not* first find the actual path of Mars about the sun, and then compute its speed in terms of the area swept out by a line from the sun to Mars. This is but one example of the difficulty in following Kepler through his book on Mars.

The Keplerian Achievement

Galileo particularly disliked the idea that solar emanations or mysterious forces acting at-a-distance could affect the earth or any part of the earth. He not only rejected Kepler's suggestion that the sun might be the origin of an attractive force moving the earth and planets (on which the first two laws of Kepler were based), but he especially rejected Kepler's suggestion that a lunar force or emanation might cause the tides. Thus he wrote:

"But among all the great men who have philosophized about this remarkable effect, I am more astonished at Kepler than at any other. Despite his open and acute mind, and though he has at his fingertips the motions attributed to the earth, he has nevertheless lent his ear and his assent to the moon's dominion over the waters, and to occult properties, and to such puerilities."

As to the harmonic law, or third law, we may ask with the voice of Galileo and his contemporaries, Is this science or numerology? Kepler already had committed himself in print to the belief that the telescope should reveal not only the four satellites of Jupiter discovered by Galileo, but two of Mars and eight of Saturn. The reason for these particular numbers was that then the number of satellites per planet would increase according to a regular geometric sequence: 1 (for the earth), 2 (for Mars), 4 (for Jupiter), 8 (for Saturn). Was not Kepler's distance-period relation something of the same pure number-juggling rather than true science? And was not evidence for the generally nonscientific aspect of Kepler's whole book to be found in the way he tried to fit the numerical aspects of the planets' motions and locations into the questions posed in the table of contents for Book Five of his *Harmony of the World?*

"1. Concerning the five regular solid figures.
  2. On the kinship between them and the harmonic ratios.
  3. Summary of astronomical doctrine necessary for speculation into the celestial harmonies.
  4. In what things pertaining to the planetary movements the simple consonances have been expressed and that all those consonances which are present in song are found in the heavens.
  5. That the clefs of the musical scale, or pitches of the system, and the genera of consonances, the major and the minor, are expressed in certain movements.
  6. That the single musical Tones or Modes are somehow expressed by the single planets.
  7. That the counterpoints or universal harmonies of all the planets can exist and be different from one another.
  8. That the four kinds of voice are expressed in the planets; soprano, contralto, tenor, and bass.
  9. Demonstration that in order to secure this harmonic arrangement, those very planetary eccentricities which any planet has as its own, and no others, had to be set up.
  10. Epilogue concerning the sun, by way of very fertile conjectures."

Below are shown the "tunes" played by the planets in the Keplerian scheme.

Fig. 29. Kepler's music of the planets, from his book Harmony of the World. *Small wonder a man of Galileo's stamp never bothered to read it!*

Surely a man of Galileo's stamp would find it hard to consider such a book a serious contribution to celestial physics.

Kepler's last major book was an *Epitome of Copernican Astronomy,* completed for publication nine years before his death in 1630. In it he defended his departures from the original Copernican system. But what is of the most interest to us is that in this book, as in the *Harmony of the World* (1619), Kepler again proudly presented his earliest discovery concerning the five regular solids and the six planets. It was, he still maintained, the reason for the number of planets being six.

It must have been almost as much work to disentangle the three laws of Kepler from the rest of his writings as to remake the discoveries. Kepler deserves credit for having been the first scientist to recognize that the Copernican concept of the earth as a planet and Galileo's discoveries demanded that there be one physics—applying equally to the celestial objects and ordinary terrestrial bodies. But, alas, Kepler remained so enmeshed in

Aristotelian physics that when he attempted to project a terrestrial physics into the heavens, the basis still came from Aristotle. Thus the major aim of Keplerian physics remained unachieved, and the first workable physics for heaven and earth derived not from Kepler but from Galileo and attained its form under the magistral guidance of Isaac Newton.

CHAPTER 7

The Grand Design—A New Physics

The publication of Isaac Newton's *Principia* in 1687 was one of the most notable events in the whole history of physical science. In it one may find the culmination of thousands of years of striving to comprehend the system of the world, the principles of force and of motion, and the physics of bodies moving in different media. It is no small testimony to the vitality of Newton's scientific genius that although the physics of the *Principia* has been altered, improved, and challenged ever since, we still set about solving most problems of celestial mechanics and the physics of gross bodies proceeding essentially as Newton did some 300 years ago. And if this is not enough to satisfy the canons of greatness, Newton was equally great as a pure mathematician. He invented the differential and integral calculus (produced simultaneously and independently by the German philosopher Gottfried Wilhelm Leibniz), which is the language of physics; he developed the binomial theorem and various properties of infinite series; and he laid the foundations for the calculus of variations. In optics Newton began the experimental study of the analysis and composition of light, showing that white light is a mixture of light of many colors, each having a characteristic index of refraction. Upon these researches have risen the science of spectroscopy and the methods of color analysis. Newton invented a reflecting telescope and so showed astronomers how to transcend the limitations of telescopes built of lenses. All in all, it was a fantastic scientific achievement—of a kind that has never been equalled.

In this book we shall deal exclusively with Newton's system of dynamics and gravitation, the central problems for which the preceding chapters have been a preparation. If you have read them carefully, you have in mind all but one of the major ingredients requisite to an understanding of the Newtonian system of the world. But even if that one were to be given—the analysis of uniform circular motion—the guiding hand of Newton would still be required to put the ingredients together. It took genius to supply the new concept of universal gravitation. Let us see what Newton actually did.

First of all, it must be understood that Galileo himself never attempted to display any scheme of mechanics that would account for the movement of the planets, or of their satellites. As for Copernicus, the *De revolutionibus* contains no important insight into a celestial mechanics. Kepler had tried to supply a celestial mechanism, but the result was never a very happy one. He held that the *anima motrix* emanating from the sun would cause planets to revolve about the sun in circles. He further supposed that magnetic interaction of sun and planet would shift the planet during an otherwise circular revolution into an elliptical orbit. Others who contemplated the problems of planetary motion proposed systems of mechanics containing certain features that were later to appear in Newtonian dynamics. One of these was Robert Hooke, who quite understandably thought that Newton should have given him more credit than a mere passing reference for having anticipated parts of the laws of dynamics and gravitation.

Newtonian Anticipations

The climactic chapter in the discovery of the mechanics of the universe starts with a pretty story. By the third quarter of the seventeenth century a group of men had become so eager to advance the new mathematical experimental sciences that they banded together to perform experiments in concert, to present problems for solution to one another, to report on their own researches and on those of others as revealed by correspondence, books, and pamphlets. Thus it came about that Robert Hooke, Edmund Halley, and Sir Christopher Wren, England's foremost architect, met to discuss the question, Under what law of force would a planet follow an elliptical orbit? From Kepler's laws—especially the third or harmonic law, but also the second or law of areas—it was clear that the sun somehow or other must control or at least affect the motion of a planet in accordance with the relative proximity of the planet to the sun. Even if the particular mechanisms proposed by Kepler (an *anima motrix* and a magnetic force) had to be rejected, there could be no doubt that some kind of planet-sun interaction keeps the planets in their courses. Furthermore, a more acute intuition than Kepler's would sense that any force emanating from the sun must spread out in all directions from that body, presumably diminishing according to the inverse of the square of its distance from the sun—as light diminishes in intensity in relation to distance. But to say this much is a very different thing from *proving* it mathematically. For to prove it would require a complete physics with mathematical methods for solving all the attendant and consequent problems. When he declined to credit authors who tossed off general statements without being able to prove them mathematically or fit them into a valid framework of dynamics, Newton was quite justified in saying, as he did of Hooke's claims: "Now is not this very fine! Mathematicians that find out, settle, and do all the business, must content themselves with being nothing but dry calculators and drudges; and another, that does nothing but pretend and grasp at all things, must carry away all the invention, as well as those that were to follow him as of those that went before."

In any event, by January 1684, Halley had concluded that the force acting on planets to keep them in their orbits "decreased in the proportion of the squares of the distances reciprocally,"

$$F \propto \frac{1}{D^2}$$

but he was not able to deduce from that hypothesis the observed motions of the celestial bodies. When Wren and Hooke met later in the month, they agreed with Halley's supposition of a solar force. Hooke boasted "that upon that principle all the laws of the celestial motions were to be [i.e., could be] demonstrated, and that he himself had done it." But despite repeated urgings and Wren's offer of a considerable monetary prize, Hooke did not—and presumably could not—produce a solution. Six months later, in August 1684, Halley decided to go to Cambridge to consult Isaac Newton. On his arrival he learned the "good news" that Newton "had brought this demonstration to perfection." Here is an almost contemporaneous account of that visit:

"Without mentioning either his own speculations, or those of Hooke and Wren, he at once indicated the object of his visit by asking Newton what would be the curve described by the planets on the supposition that gravity diminished as the square of the distance. Newton immediately answered, *an Ellipse*. Struck with joy and amazement, Halley asked him how he knew it? 'Why,' replied he, 'I have calculated it'; and being asked for the calculation, he could not find it, but promised to send it to him. After Halley left Cambridge, Newton endeavoured to reproduce the calculation, but did not succeed in obtaining the same result. Upon examining carefully his diagram and calculations, he found that in describing an ellipse coarsely with his own hand, he had drawn the two axes of the curve instead of two conjugate diameters somewhat inclined to one another. When this mistake was corrected he obtained the result which he had announced to Halley."

Spurred on by Halley's visit, Newton resumed work on a subject that had commanded his attention in his twenties when he had laid the foundations of his other great scientific discoveries: the nature of white light and color and the differential and integral calculus. He now put his investigations in order, made great progress, and in the fall term of the year, discussed his research in a series of lectures on dynamics which he gave at Cambridge University, as required by his professorship. Eventually, with Halley's encouragement, the draft of these lectures, *De motu corporum,* grew into one of the greatest and most influential books any man has yet conceived. Many a scientist has echoed the sentiment which Halley expressed in the ode he wrote as a preface to Newton's *Principia* (or, to give Newton's masterpiece its full title, *Philosophiae naturalis principia mathematica, The Mathematical Principles of Natural Philosophy,* London, 1687):

> Then ye who now on heavenly far,
> Come celebrate with me in song the name
> Of Newton, to the Muses dear; for he
> Unlocked the hidden treasuries of Truth:
> So richly through his mind had Phoebus cast
> The radiance of his own divinity.
> Nearer the gods no mortal may approach.

The Principia

The *Principia* is divided into three parts or "books"; we shall concentrate on the first and third. In Book One Newton develops the general principles of the dynamics of moving bodies, and in Book Three he applies the principles to the mechanism of the universe. Book Two deals with fluid mechanics, the theory of waves and other aspects of physics.

In Book One, following the Preface, a set of Definitions, and a discussion of the nature of time and space, Newton presented the "Axioms, or Laws of Motion":

Law I

Every body continues in its state of rest, or of uniform motion in a right [straight] line, unless it is compelled to change that state by forces impressed upon it.

Law II

The change of motion is proportional to the motive force impressed; and is made in the direction of the right line in which that force is impressed.

Observe that if a body is in "uniform motion in a right line," a force at right angles to the direction of motion of the body will not affect the forward motion. This follows from the fact that the acceleration is always in the same direction as the force producing it, so that the acceleration in this case is at right angles to the direction of motion. Thus in the toy train experiment of Chapter 5, the chief force acting is the downward force of gravity, producing a vertical acceleration. The ball, whether moving forward or at rest, is thus caused to slow down in its upward motion until it comes to rest, and then be speeded up or accelerated on the way down.

A comparison of the two sets of photographs shows

that the upward and downward motions are exactly the
same whether the train is at rest or in uniform motion.
In the forward direction there is no effect of weight or
gravity, since this acts only in a downward direction. The
only force in the forward or horizontal direction is the
small amount of air friction, which is almost negligible;
so one may say that in the horizontal direction there is
no force acting. According to Newton's first law of motion, the ball will continue to move in the forward direction with "uniform motion in a right line" just as the
train does—a fact you can check by inspecting the photograph. The ball remains above the locomotive whether
the train is at rest or in uniform motion in a straight line.
This law of motion is sometimes called the "Principle of
Inertia," and the property that material bodies have of
continuing in a state of rest or of uniform motion in a
right line is sometimes known as the body's inertia.*

Newton illustrated Law I by reference to projectiles
which continue in their forward motions "so far as they
are not retarded by the resistance of the air, or impelled
downward by the force of gravity," and he referred also
to "the greater bodies of planets and comets." At this
one stroke Newton postulated the opposite view of
Aristotelian physics. In the latter no celestial body could
move uniformly in a straight line in the absence of a
force, because this would be a "violent" motion and so
contrary to its nature. Nor could a terrestrial object, as
we have seen, move along its "natural" straight line
without an external mover or an internal motive force.

* The earliest known statement of this law was made by René
Descartes in a work that he did not publish. It appeared in print
for the first time in a work by Pierre Gassendi. But prior to
Newton's *Principia* there was no completely developed inertial
physics. It is not without significance that this book of Descartes
was based on the Copernican point of view; Descartes suppressed
it on learning of the condemnation of Galileo. Gassendi likewise
was a Copernican. He actually made experiments with objects
let fall from moving ships and moving carriages to test Galileo's
conclusions.

Newton, presenting a physics that applies simultaneously to both terrestrial and celestial objects, stated that in the absence of a force bodies do not necessarily stand still as Aristotle supposed, but they may move at constant rectilinear speed. This "indifference" of all sorts of bodies to rest or uniform straight line motion in the absence of a force clearly is an advanced form of Galileo's statement in his *Letters on the Solar Spots* (page 125), the difference being that in that work Galileo was writing about uniform motion along a great spherical surface concentric with the earth.

Newton said of the Laws of Motion that they were "such principles as have been received by mathematicians, and . . . confirmed by [an] abundance of experiments. By the first two Laws and the first two Corollaries, Galileo discovered that the descent of bodies varies as the square of the time and that the motion of projectiles is in the curve of a parabola: experience agreeing with both, unless so far as these motions are a little retarded by the resistance of the air." The "two Corollaries" deal with methods used by Galileo and many of his predecessors to combine two different forces or two independent motions. Fifty years after the publication of Galileo's *Two New Sciences* it was difficult for Newton, who had already established an inertial physics to conceive that Galileo could have come as close as he had to the concept of inertia without having taken full leave of circularity and having stated a true principle of linear inertia.

Newton was being very generous to Galileo because, however it may be argued that Galileo "really did" have the law of inertia or Newton's Law I, a great stretch of the imagination is required to assign any credit to Galileo for Law II. This law has two parts. In the second half of Newton's statement of Law II the "change in motion" produced by an "impressed" or "motive" force —whether that be a change in the speed with which a body moves or a change in the direction in which it is moving—is said to be "in the direction of the right line in which that force is impressed." This much is certainly implied in Galileo's analysis of projectile motion because Galileo assumed that in the forward direction there was no acceleration because there was no horizontal force, except the negligible action of air friction; but in the vertical direction there was an acceleration or continual increase of downward speed, because of the downward-acting weight force. But the first part of Law II—that the change in the magnitude of the motion is related to the motive force—is something else again; only a Newton could have seen it in Galileo's studies of falling bodies. This part of the law says that if an object were to be acted on first by one force F_1 and then by some other force F_2, the accelerations or changes in speed produced, A_1 and A_2, would be proportional to the forces, or that

$$\frac{F_1}{F_2} = \frac{A_1}{A_2} \text{ , or}$$

$$\frac{F_1}{A_1} = \frac{F_2}{A_2}$$

But in analyzing falling, Galileo was dealing with a situation in which only one force acted on each body, its weight W, and the acceleration it produced was g the acceleration of a freely falling body.

While Aristotle had said that a given force gives an object a certain characteristic speed, Newton now said that a given force always produces in that body a definite acceleration A. To find the speed V, we must know how long a time T the force acted, or how long the object had been accelerated, so that Galileo's law

$$V = AT$$

may be applied.

At this point let us try a thought-experiment, in which

we assume we have two cubes of aluminum, one just twice the volume of the other. (Incidentally, to "duplicate" a cube—or make a cube having exactly twice the volume as some given cube—is as impossible within the framework of Euclidean geometry as to trisect an angle or to square a circle.) We now subject the smaller cube to a series of forces F_1, F_2, F_3, . . . and determine the corresponding accelerations A_1, A_2, A_3, . . . In accordance with Law II, we would find that there is a certain constant value of the ratio of force to acceleration

$$\frac{F_1}{A_1} = \frac{F_2}{A_2} = \frac{F_3}{A_3} = \ldots = m_s$$

which for this object we may call m_s. We now repeat the operations with the larger cube and find that the same set of forces F_1, F_2, F_3, . . . respectively produces *another* set of accelerations a_1, a_2, a_3, . . . In accordance with Newton's second law, the force-acceleration ratio is again a constant which for this object we may call m_l

$$\frac{F_1}{a_1} = \frac{F_2}{a_2} = \frac{F_3}{a_3} = \ldots = m_l$$

For the larger object the constant proves to be just twice as large as the constant obtained for the smaller one and, in general, so long as we deal with a single variety of matter like pure aluminum, *this constant* is proportional to the volume and so *is a measure of the amount of aluminum in any sample*. This particular constant is a measure of an object's resistance to acceleration, or a measure of the tendency of that object to stay as it is—either at rest, or in motion in a straight line. For observe that m_l was twice m_s; to give both objects the same acceleration or change in motion the force required for the larger object is just twice what it must be for the smaller. The tendency of any object to continue in its state of motion (at constant speed in a straight line) or its state of rest is called its *inertia*; hence,

Newton's Law I is also called the principle of inertia. The constant determined by finding the constant force-acceleration ratio for any given body may thus be called *the body's inertia*. But for our aluminum blocks this same constant is also a measure of the "quantity of matter" in the object, which is called its *mass*. We now make precise the condition that two objects of different material—say one of brass and the other of wood—shall have the same "quantity of matter": it is that they have the *same mass* as determined by the force-acceleration ratio, or the *same inertia*.

In ordinary life, we do not compare the "quantity of matter" in objects in terms of their inertias, but in terms of their weight. Newtonian physics makes it clear why we can, and through its clarification we are able to understand why at any place on the earth two unequal weights in a vacuum fall at the same rate. But we may observe that in at least one common situation we always compare the inertias of objects rather than their weights. This happens when a person hefts two objects to find which is heavier, or has the greater mass. He does not hold them out to see which pulls down more on his arm; instead, he moves them up and down to find which is easier to move. In this way he determines which has the greater resistance to a change in its state of motion in a straight line or of rest—that is, which has the greater inertia.

Final Formulation of the Law of Inertia

At one point in his *Discourses and Demonstrations Concerning Two New Sciences* Galileo imagined the motion of a ball rolling along a plane "with a motion which is uniform and perpetual, provided the plane has no limits." A plane without limit is all right for a pure mathematician, who is a Platonist in any case. But Galileo was a man who combined just such a Platonism with a concern for applications to the real world of sensory experience. In the *Two New Sciences* Galileo was not interested in abstractions as such, but in the analysis of real motions on or near the earth. So we understand that having talked about a plane without limit, he does not continue with such a fancy, but asks what would happen on such a plane if it were a real earthly plane, which for him means that it is "limited and elevated." The ball, in the real world of physics, falls off the plane and begins to fall to the ground. In this case,

> ". . . the moving particle, which we imagine to be a heavy one, will on passing over the edge of the plane acquire, in addition to its previous uniform and perpetual motion, a downward propensity due to its own weight; so that the resulting motion which I call projection is compounded of one which is uniform and horizontal and of another which is vertical and naturally accelerated."

Unlike Galileo, Newton made a clear separation between the world of abstract mathematics and the world of physics, which he still called philosophy. Thus the *Principia* included both "mathematical principles" as such and those that could be applied in "natural philosophy," but Galileo's *Two New Sciences* included only those mathematical conditions exemplified in nature. For instance, Newton plainly knew that the attractive force exerted by the sun on a planet varies as the inverse-square of the distance,

$$F \propto \frac{1}{D^2}$$

but in Book One of the *Principia* he explored the consequences not only of this particular force but of others with quite different dependence on the distance, including

$$F \propto D$$

$$F \propto \frac{1}{D^3}$$

"The System of the World"

At the beginning of Book Three, which was devoted to "The System of the World," Newton explained how it differed from the preceding two, which had been dealing with "The Motion of Bodies,"

> "In the preceding Books I have laid down . . . principles not philosophical [pertaining to physics] but mathematical: such, namely, as we may build our reasonings upon in philosophical inquiries. These principles are laws and conditions of certain motions, and powers or forces, which chiefly have respect to philosophy; but, lest they should have appeared of themselves dry and barren, I have illustrated them here and there with some philosophical scholiums, giving an account of such things as are of a more general nature, and which philosophy seems chiefly to be founded on: such as the density and the resistance of bodies, spaces void of all bodies, and the motion of light and sounds. It remains that, from the same principles, I now demonstrate the System of the World."

I believe it fair to say that it was the freedom to consider problems either in a purely mathematical way or in a "philosophical" (or physical) way that enabled Newton to express the first law and to develop a complete inertial physics. After all, physics as a science may be developed in a mathematical way but it always must rest on experience—and experience never shows us pure inertial motion. Even in the limited examples of linear inertia discussed by Galileo, there was always some air friction and the motion ceased almost at once, as when a projectile strikes the ground. In the whole range of physics explored by Galileo there is no example of a physical object that has even a component of pure inertial motion for more than a very short time. It was perhaps for this reason that Galileo never framed a general law of inertia. He was too much a physicist.

But as a mathematician Newton could easily conceive of a body's moving along a straight line at constant speed forever. The concept "forever," which implies an infinite universe, held no terror for him. Observe that his statement of the law of inertia, that it is the natural condition for bodies to move in straight lines at constant speed forever, occurs in Book One of the *Principia,* the portion said by him to be mathematical rather than physical. Now, if it is the natural condition of motion for bodies to move uniformly in straight lines, then this kind of inertial motion must characterize the planets. But the planets do not move in straight lines, but rather along ellipses. Using a kind of Galilean approach to this single problem, Newton could say that the planets must therefore be subject to two motions: one inertial (along a straight line at constant speed) and one always at right angles to that straight line drawing each planet toward its orbit.

Though not moving in a straight line, each planet nevertheless represents the best example of inertial motion observable in the universe. But for that component of inertial motion, the force that continually draws the planet away from the straight line would draw the planet in toward the sun until the two bodies collided. Newton once used this argument to prove the existence of God. If the planets had not received a push to give them an inertial (or tangential) component of motion, he said, the solar attractive force would not draw them into an orbit but instead would move each planet in a straight line toward the sun itself. Hence the universe could not be explained in terms of matter alone.

For Galileo pure circular motion could still be inertial, as in the example of an object on or near the surface of the earth. But for Newton pure circular motion was not inertial; it was accelerated and required a force for its continuance. Thus it was Newton who finally shattered the bonds of "circularity" which still had held Galileo in thrall. And so we may understand that it was Newton who showed how to build a celestial mechanics based on the laws of motion: since their elliptical (or almost circular) orbital motion is not purely inertial, it requires the constant action of a force, which turns out to be the force of universal gravitation.

Thus Newton, again unlike Galileo, set out to "demonstrate the System of the World," or—as we would say today—to show how the general laws of terrestrial motion may be applied to the planets and to their satellites.

In the first theorem of the *Principia* Newton showed that if a body were to move with a purely inertial motion, then with respect to any point not on the line of motion, the law of equal areas must apply. In other words, a line drawn from any such body to such a point will sweep out equal areas in equal times. Conceive a body moving with purely inertial motion along the straight line of which *PQ* is a segment. Then in a set of equal time intervals (Fig. 30) the body will move through equal distances *AB, BC, DC*, . . . because, as Galileo showed, in uniform motion a body moves through equal distances in equal times. But observe that

Fig. 30.

a line from the point O sweeps out equal areas in these equal times, or that the areas of triangles OAB, OBC, OCD, . . . are equal. The reason is that the area of a triangle is one-half the product of its altitude and its base; and all these triangles have the same altitude OH and equal bases. Since

$$AB = BC = CD = . . .$$

it is true that

$$½AB \times OH = ½BC \times OH = ½CD \times OH = ...$$

or

area of $\triangle$ $OAB =$ area of $\triangle$ $OBC =$ area of $\triangle$ $OCD = . . .$

Thus the very first theorem proved in the *Principia* showed that purely inertial motion leads to a law of equal areas, and so is related to Kepler's second law. Newton then proved that if at regular intervals of time, a body moving with purely inertial motion were to receive a momentary impulse (a force acting for an instant only), all these impulses being directed toward the same point S, then the body would move in each of the equal time-intervals between impulses so that a line from it to S would sweep out equal areas. This situation is shown in Fig. 31. When the body reaches the point B it receives an impulse toward S. The new motion is a combination of the original motion along AB and a motion toward S, which produces a uniform rectilinear motion toward C, etc.: The triangles SAB, SBC, and SCD . . . have the same area. The next step, according to Newton, is as follows:

". . . Now let the number of those triangles be augmented, and their breadth diminished *in infinitum;* and (by Cor. iv, Lem. iii) their ultimate perimeter ADF will be a curved line: and therefore the cen-

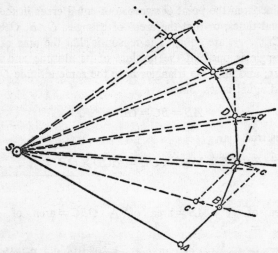

Fig. 31. If at B the body had received no impulse, it would, during time T, have moved along the continuation of AB to c. The impulse at B, however, gives the body a component of motion toward S. During T if the body's only motion came from that impulse, it would have moved from B to c'. The combination of these two movements, Bc and Bc', results during time T in a movement from B to C. Newton proved that the area of the triangle SBC is equal to the area of the triangle SBc. Hence, even when there is an impulsive force directed toward S, the law of equal areas holds.

tripetal force, by which the body is continually drawn back from the tangent of this curve, will act continually; and any described areas *SADS, SAFS,* which are always proportional to the times of description, will, in this case also, be proportional to those times. Q.E.D."

In this way Newton proceeded to prove:

PROPOSITION I. THEOREM I

The areas which revolving bodies describe by radii drawn to an immovable centre of force do lie in the same immovable planes, and are proportional to the times in which they are described.

In simple language, Newton proved in the first theorem of Book One of the *Principia* that if a body is continually drawn toward some center of force, its otherwise inertial motion will be transformed into motion along a curve, and that a line from the center of force to the body will sweep out equal areas in equal times. In Proposition II (Theorem II) he proved that if a body moves along a curve so that the areas described by a line from the body to any point are proportional to the times, there must be a "central" (centripetal) force continuously urging the body toward that point. The significance of Kepler's Law II does not appear until Proposition XI when Newton sets out to find "the law of the centripetal force tending to the focus of the ellipse." This force varies "inversely as the square of the distance." Then Newton proves that if a body moving in an hyperbola or in a parabola is acted on by a centripetal force tending to the focus, the force still varies inversely as the square of the distance. Several theorems later, in Proposition XVII, Newton proves the converse, that if a body moves subject to a centripetal force varying inversely as the square of the distance, the path of the body must be a conic section: an ellipse, a parabola, or hyperbola.

We may note that Newton has treated Kepler's laws exactly in the same order as Kepler himself: first the law of areas as a general theorem, and only later the particular shape of planetary orbits as ellipses. What seemed at first to be a rather odd way of proceeding has been shown to represent a fundamental logical progression of a kind that is the opposite of the sequence that would have been followed in an empirical or observational approach.

In Newton's reasoning about the action of a centripetal force on a body moving with purely inertial motion, mathematical analysis, for the first time, disclosed the true meaning of Kepler's "second law" of equal areas! Newton's reasoning showed that this law implied a center of force for the motion of each planet. Since the equal areas in planetary motion are reckoned with respect to the sun, Kepler's second law becomes in Newton's treatment the basis for proving rigorously that a central force emanating from the sun attracts all the planets.

So much for the problem raised by Halley. Had Newton stopped his work at this point, we would still admire his achievement enormously. But Newton went on and the results were even more outstanding.

The Master-stroke: Universal Gravitation

In Book Three of the *Principia*, Newton showed that as Jupiter's satellites move in orbits around their planet, a line from Jupiter to each satellite will "describe areas proportional to the times of description" and that the ratio of the squares of their times to the cubes of their mean distances from the center of Jupiter is a constant, although a constant having a different value from the constant for the motion of the planets. Thus if T_1, T_2, T_3, T_4 be the periodic times of the satellites, and a_1, a_2, a_3, a_4 be their respective mean distances from Jupiter,

$$\frac{(a_1)^3}{(T_1)^2} = \frac{(a_2)^3}{(T_2)^2} = \frac{(a_3)^3}{(T_3)^2} = \frac{(a_4)^3}{(T_4)^2}$$

Not only do these laws of Kepler apply to the Jovian system, but they also apply to the five satellites of Saturn known to Newton—a result wholly unknown to Kepler. The third law of Kepler could not be applied to the earth's moon because there is only one moon, but Newton did state that its motion accorded to the law of equal areas. Hence, one may see that there is a central force, varying as the inverse-square of the distance, that holds each planet to an orbit around the sun and each planetary satellite to an orbit around its planet.

Now Newton makes the master-stroke. He shows that a single universal force (a) keeps the planets in their orbits around the sun, (b) holds the satellites in their orbits, (c) causes falling objects to descend as observed, (d) holds objects on the earth, and (e) causes the tides. It is the force called *universal gravitation,* and its fundamental law may be written

$$F = G \frac{mm'}{D^2}$$

This law says that between any two bodies whatsoever, of masses m and m', wherever they may be in the universe, separated by a distance D, there is a force of attraction which is *mutual,* and each body attracts the other with a force of identical magnitude, which is *directly proportional to the product of the two masses and inversely proportional to the square of the distance between them.* G is a constant of proportionality, and it has the same value in all circumstances—whether in the mutual attraction of a stone and the earth, of the earth and the moon, of the sun and Jupiter, of one star and another, or of two pebbles on a beach. This constant G is called the *constant of universal gravitation* and may be compared to other "universal" constants—of which there are not very many in the whole of science—such as c, the speed of light, which figures so prominently in Relativity, or h, Planck's constant, which is so basic in Quantum Theory.

How did Newton find his law? It is difficult to tell in detail, but we can reconstruct some of the basic aspects of the discovery.

From a later memorandum (about 1714), we learn that Newton as a young man "began to think of gravity extending to the orb of the moon, and having found out how to estimate the force with which a globe revolving within a sphere presses the surface of the sphere, from Kepler's Rule of the periodical times of the planets being in a sesquialterate proportion [i.e., as the ⅔ power] of their distances from the centres of their orbs, I deduced that the forces which keep the planets in their orbs must [be] reciprocally as the squares of their distances from the centres about which they revolve: and thereby compared the force requisite to keep the moon in her orb with the force of gravity at the surface of the earth, and found them answer [i.e., agree] pretty nearly."

With this statement as guide, let us consider first a globe of mass m and speed v moving along a circle of radius r. Then, as Newton found out, and as the great Dutch physicist Christian Huygens (1629–1695) also discovered (and to Newton's chagrin, published first), there must be a central acceleration, of magnitude v^2/r. That is, an acceleration follows from the fact that the globe is not at rest nor moving at constant speed in a straight line; from Law I and Law II, there must be a force and hence an acceleration. We shall not prove that this acceleration has a magnitude v^2/r, but that it is directed toward the center you can see if you whirl a ball in a circle at the end of a string. A force is needed to pull the ball constantly toward the center, and from Law II the acceleration must always have the same direction as the accelerating force. Thus for a planet of mass m, moving approximately in a circle of radius r at speed v, there must be a central force F of magnitude

$$F = mA = m \frac{v^2}{r}$$

If T is the period, or time for the planet to move through 360°, then in time T the planet moves once around a circle of radius r, or through a circumference of $2\pi r$. Hence the speed v is $2\pi r/T$, and

$$F = mA = mv^2 \times \frac{1}{r} = m \left[\frac{2\pi r}{T}\right]^2 \times \frac{1}{r}$$

$$= m \times \frac{4\pi^2 r^2}{T^2} \times \frac{1}{r}$$

$$= m \times \frac{4\pi^2 r^2}{T^2} \times \frac{1}{r} \times \frac{r}{r}$$

$$= \frac{4\pi^2 m \times r^3}{T^2 \times r^2} = \frac{4\pi^2 m}{r^2} \times \frac{r^3}{T^2}$$

Since for every planet in the solar system, r^3/T^2 has the same value K (by Kepler's rule or third law),

$$F = \frac{4\pi^2 m}{r^2} \times K = 4\pi^2 K \frac{m}{r^2}$$

The radius r of the circular orbit corresponds in reality to D the average distance of a planet from the sun. Hence, for any planet the law of force keeping it in its orbit must be

$$F = 4\pi^2 K \frac{m}{D^2}$$

where m is the mass of the planet, D is the average distance of the planet from the sun, K is "Kepler's constant" for the solar system (equal to the cube of the mean distance of any planet from the sun divided by the square of its period of revolution), and F is the force with which the sun attracts the planet and draws it continually off its purely inertial path into an ellipse. Thus far mathematics and logic may lead a man of superior wit who knows the Newtonian laws of motion and the principles of circular motion.

But now we rewrite the equation as

$$F = \left[\frac{4\pi^2 K}{M_s} \right] \frac{M_s m}{D^2}$$

where M_s is the mass of the sun and say that the quantity

$$\frac{4\pi^2 K}{M_s} = G$$

is a *universal constant,* that the law

$$F = G\frac{M_s m}{D^2}$$

is not limited to the force between the sun and a planet.
It applies also to every pair of objects in the universe,
M_s and m becoming the masses m and m' of those two
objects and D becoming the distance between them:

$$F = G\frac{mm'}{D^2}$$

There is no mathematics—whether algebra, geometry,
or the calculus—to justify this bold step. One can say of
it only that it is one of those triumphs that humble ordinary men in the presence of genius. And just think
what this law implies. For instance, this book that you
hold in your hands attracts the sun in a calculable degree; it is the same force that makes the moon follow its
orbit and an apple fall from the tree. Late in life Newton
said it was this last comparison that inspired his great
discovery.

The moon (see Fig. 32) if not attracted by the earth
would have a purely inertial motion and in a small time
t would move uniformly along a straight line (a tangent)
from A to B. It does not, said Newton, because while
its inertial motion would have carried it from A to B,
the gravitational attraction of the earth will have made
it fall toward the earth from the line AB to C. Thus the
moon's departure from a purely inertial rectilinear path
is caused by its continual "falling" toward the earth—
and its falling is just like the falling of an apple. Is this
true? Well, Newton put the proposition to a test, as
follows:

Why does an apple of mass m fall to the earth? It does
so, we may now say, because there is a force of universal
gravitation between it and the earth, whose mass is M_e.
But what is the distance between the earth and the apple?

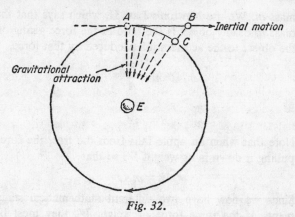

Fig. 32.

Is it the few feet from the apple to the ground? Newton eventually was able to prove that the attraction between a small object and a more or less homogeneous and more or less spherical body is exactly the same as if all the large mass of the body were concentrated at its geometric center. This theorem means that in considering the mutual attraction of earth and apple, the distance D in the law of universal gravitation may be taken to be the earth's radius, R_e. Hence the law states that the attraction between the earth and an apple is:

$$F = G\frac{mM_e}{R_e{}^2},$$

where m is the mass of the apple, M_e the mass of the earth and R_e the earth's radius. But this is an expression for the *weight* W of the apple, because the weight of any terrestrial object is merely the magnitude of the force with which it is gravitationally attracted by the earth. Thus,

$$W = G\frac{mM_e}{R_e{}^2}.$$

There is a second way of writing an equation for the weight of an apple or of any other terrestrial object of mass m. We use Newton's Law II, which says that the mass m of any object is the ratio of the force acting on the object to the acceleration produced by that force,

$$m = \frac{F}{A}$$

or

$$F = mA.$$

Note that when an apple falls from the tree, the force pulling it down is its weight W, so that

$$W = mA.$$

Since we now have two different mathematical statements of the same force or weight W, they must be equal to each other, or

$$mA = G\frac{mM_e}{R_e^2}$$

and we can divide both sides by m to get

$$A = G\frac{M_e}{R_e^2}.$$

So, by Newtonian principles, we have at once explained why at any spot on this earth all objects—whatever their mass m or weight W may be—will have the same acceleration A when they fall freely, as in a vacuum. The last equation shows that this acceleration of free fall is determined by the mass M_e and radius R_e of the earth and a universal constant G, none of which *depends in any way* on the particular mass m or weight W of the falling body.

Now let us write the last equation in a slightly different way,

$$A = G\frac{M_e}{D_e^2}$$

where D_e stands for the distance from the center of the earth. At or near the earth's surface D_e is merely the earth's radius R_e. Now consider a body placed at a distance D_e of 60 earth-radii from the earth's center. With what acceleration A' will it fall toward the center of the earth? The acceleration A' will be

$$A' = G\frac{M_e}{(60\,R_e)^2} = G\frac{M_e}{3600\,R_e^2} = \frac{1}{3600}\,G\frac{M_e}{R_e^2}$$

We just saw that at the surface of the earth an apple or any other object will have a downward acceleration equal to $G\dfrac{M_e}{R_e^2}$, and now we have proved that an object at 60 earth-radii will have an acceleration just $\frac{1}{3600}$th of that value. On the average, a body at the earth's surface falls in one second toward the earth through a distance of 16.08 feet, so that out at a distance of 60 earth-radii from the earth's center a body should fall

$$\frac{1}{3600} \times 16.08 \text{ feet} = \frac{1}{3600} \times 16.08 \times 12 \text{ inches} = 0.0536 \text{ inches.}$$

It happens that there is a body out in space at a distance of 60 earth-radii and so Newton had a subject for testing his theory of universal gravitation. If the same gravitational force makes both the apple and the moon fall, then in one second the moon must have fallen through 0.0536 inches from its inertial path to stay on its orbit. A rough computation, based on the simplifying assumptions that the moon's orbit is a perfect circle and that the moon moves uniformly without being affected by the gravitational attraction of the sun, yields a distance fallen in one second of 0.0539 inches—or a remarkable agreement to within 0.0003 inches! Another way of seeing how closely observation agrees with theory is to observe that the two values differ by 3 parts in about 500, which is the same as 6 parts in 1000 or 0.6 parts per hundred (0.6 per cent). Another way of seeing how this calculation can be made (perhaps following the lead Newton himself gave in the quotation on page 171f.) is as follows:

1) For a body on earth (the apple)

$$g = \frac{GM_e}{R_e^2}$$

2) For the moon (Kepler's Third Law)

$$K = \frac{R_m^3}{T_m^2} = \frac{GM_e}{4\pi^2}$$

Then

$$g = \frac{4\pi^2 R_m^3}{R_e^2 T_m^2} = 4\pi^2 \left[\frac{R_m}{R_e} \right]^3 \frac{R_e}{T_m^2}$$

Put

$$\frac{R_m}{R_e} = 60, R_e = 4{,}000 \times 5{,}280 \text{ feet}$$

$$T_m = 28d = 28 \times 24 \times 3600 \text{ sec}$$

Gives

$$g = 31 \text{ ft/sec}^2$$

Newton said, in the autobiographical memorandum I have quoted, that he "compared the force requisite to keep the moon in her orb with the force of gravity at the surface of the earth."

In Book III of the *Principia*, Newton shows that the moon, in order to keep along its observed orbit, falls away from its straight line inertial path, through a distance of $15\frac{1}{12}$ Paris feet (an old measure) in every minute. Imagine the moon, he says, "deprived of all motion to be let go, so as to descend toward the earth with the impulse of all that force by which . . . it is retained in its orb." In one minute of time it will descend through the same distance that it does when this descent occurs together with the normal inertial motion. Next, assume that this motion toward the earth is due to gravity, a force that varies inversely as the square of the distance. Then, at the surface of the earth this force would be greater by a factor 60×60 than at the moon's orbit. Since the acceleration is by Newton's Second Law, proportional to the accelerating force, a body brought from the moon's orbit to the earth's surface would have an increase in its acceleration of 60×60. Thus, Newton argues, if gravity is a force varying inversely as the square of the distance, a body at the earth's surface should fall through a distance of $60 \times 60 \times 15\frac{1}{12}$ Paris feet in one minute, or $15\frac{1}{12}$ Paris feet in one second.

From Huygens' pendulum experiment Newton obtained the result that on earth (at the latitude of Paris) a body falls just about that far. Thus it is proved that it is the force of the earth's gravity that retains the moon in its orbit. In making the computation, Newton predicted from observations of the moon's motion and from gravitation theory that the distance fallen by a body on earth in one second would be 15 Paris feet, 1 inch and $1\frac{4}{9}$ lines (1 line = $\frac{1}{12}$ inch). Huygen's result for free fall at Paris was 15 Paris feet, 1 inch, $1\frac{7}{9}$ lines. The difference was $\frac{3}{9}$ or $\frac{1}{3}$ of a line and hence $\frac{1}{36}$ of an inch— a very small number indeed. By the time he wrote the *Principia,* he had found a far better agreement between theory and observation than in that rough test he had made twenty years earlier.

Newton said that in this test observation agreed with prediction "pretty nearly." Two factors were involved. First, he chose a poor value of the earth's radius and so obtained bad numerical results, agreeing only roughly or "pretty nearly." Second, since he had not then been able to prove rigorously that a homogeneous sphere attracts gravitationally as if all its mass were concentrated at its center, the proof was at best rough and approximate.

But this test proved to Newton that his concept of universal gravitation was valid. You can appreciate how remarkable it was when you consider the nature of the constant G. We saw earlier that $G = \dfrac{4\pi^2 K}{M_s}$ and we may well ask what either K (the cube of any planet's distance from the sun divided by the square of the periodic time of that planet's revolution about the sun) or M_s (the mass of the sun) has to do with either the earth's pull on a stone or the earth's pull on the moon. If the fact that the earth happens to be within the solar system lessens the wonder that G should apply to the stone and the moon, consider a system of double stars located millions of light-years away from the solar system. Such a pair of stars may form an eclipsing binary, in which one of the stars encircles the other as the moon encircles the earth. Way out there, beyond any possible influence of the sun, the same constant $G = \dfrac{4\pi^2 K}{M_s}$ applies to the attraction of each of the stars by the other. This is a universal constant *in spite of the fact* that in the form in which Newton discovered it, it was based on elements in *our solar system*. Evidently, the act of dividing the Kepler constant by the mass of the central body about which the others revolve eliminates any special aspects of that particular system—whether of planets revolving about the earth, or satellites revolving about Jupiter or Saturn.

The Dimensions of the Achievement

A few further achievements of Newtonian dynamics, or gravitation theory, will enable us to comprehend its heroic dimensions. Suppose the earth were not quite a perfect sphere, but were oblate—flattened at the poles and bulging at the equator. Consider now the acceleration A of a freely falling body at a pole, at the equator and at two intermediate points a and b. Clearly the "radius" R of the earth, or distance from the center, would increase from the pole to the equator, so that

$$R_p < R_b < R_a < R_e.$$

As a result the acceleration A of free fall at those places would have different values:

$$A_p = G\frac{M_e}{R_p{}^2}; \quad A_b = G\frac{M_e}{R_b{}^2}; \quad A_a = \frac{M_e}{R_a{}^2}; \quad A_e = \frac{M_e}{R_e{}^2},$$

so that

$$A_p > A_b > A_a > A_e$$

The following data, obtained from actual experiment, show the acceleration varies with latitude:

Latitude	Acceleration of free fall	
0° (equator)	978.039 cm/sec²	32.0878 ft/sec²
20°	978.641	32.1076
40°	980.171	32.1578
60°	981.918	32.2151
90°	983.217	32.2577

In Newton's day, the acceleration of free fall was found by determining the length of a seconds pendulum —one that has a period of 2 seconds. The equation for the period T of a common pendulum swinging through a short arc is

$$T = 2\pi\sqrt{\frac{l}{g}}$$

where l is the length of the pendulum (computed from the point of support to the center of the bob) and g is the acceleration of free fall. Halley found that when he went from London to St. Helena it was necessary to shorten the length of his pendulum in order to have it continue to beat seconds. Newton's mechanics not only explains this variation, but it leads to a prediction of the shape of the earth, an oblate spheroid, flattened at the poles and bulging at the equator.

The variations in g, the acceleration of free fall, lead to variations in the weight of any physical object transported from one latitude to another. A complete analysis of this variation in weight requires the consideration of a second factor, the force arising from the rotation of the object along with the earth. The factor that enters here is v^2/r where v is the linear speed along a circle and r the circle's radius. At different latitudes, there will be different values of both v and r. Furthermore, to relate the rotational effect to weight, a component must be taken along a line from the center of the earth to the position in question, since the rotational effect occurs in the plane of circular motion, or along a parallel of latitude. It is because of these rotational forces that the earth, according to Newtonian physics, acquired its shape.

A second consequence of the equatorial bulge is the precession of the equinoxes. In actual fact, the difference between the polar and equatorial radii of the earth may not seem very great

equatorial radius = 6378.388 km = 3963.44 miles
polar radius = 6356.909 km = 3949.99 miles

But if we represent the earth with an 18-inch globe, the difference between the smallest and greatest diameters would be about $\frac{1}{16}$th of an inch. Newton showed that precession occurs because the earth is spinning on an axis inclined to the plane of its orbit, the plane of the ecliptic. In addition to the gravitational attraction that keeps the earth in its orbit, the sun exerts a pull on the bulge, thus tending to straighten the axis. The sun tends to make the earth's axis perpendicular to the plane of the ecliptic (Fig. 33A) or make the plane of the bulge coincide with the plane of the ecliptic. At the same time the moon's pull tends to make the plane of the bulge coincide with the plane of its orbit (inclined at about 5° to the plane of the ecliptic). If the earth were a perfect sphere the pull on it of sun or moon would be symmetrical and there would be no tendency for the axis of rotation to "straighten out"; the lines of action of the gravitational pulls of sun and moon would pass through the earth's center.

Fig. 33.

Now it is a result in Newtonian physics that if a force is exerted so as to change the orientation of the axis of a spinning body, the effect will be that the axis itself, rather than changing its orientation, will undergo a conical motion. This effect may be seen in a spinning top. The axis of rotation is usually not absolutely vertical. The weight of the top tends therefore to turn the axis about the spinning point so as to make the axis horizontal. The weight tends to produce a rotation whose axis is at right angles to that of the top's spin, and the result

is the conical motion of the axis shown in Fig. 33B. The
phenomenon of precession had been known since its
discovery in the second century B.C. by Hipparchus, but
its cause had been wholly unknown before Newton.
Newton's explanation not only resolved an ancient mystery, but was an example of how one could predict the
precise shape of the earth by applying theory to astronomical observations. Newton's predictions were verified when the French mathematician Pierre L. M. de
Maupertuis measured the length of a degree of arc along
a meridian in Lapland and compared the result with the
length of a degree along the meridian nearer the equator.
The result was an impressive victory for the new science.

Yet another achievement of the Newtonian theory
was a general explanation of the tides relating them to
gravitational action of the sun and moon on the waters
of the oceans. We may well understand the spirit of ad-
miration that inspired Alexander Pope's famous couplet

> Nature and Nature's Laws lay hid in night
> God said, Let Newton be, and all was light.

In seeing how the Newtonian mechanics enabled man
to explain the motions of planets, moons, falling stones,
tides, trains, automobiles, and anything else that is accelerated—speeded up, slowed down, started in its motion or stopped—we have solved our original problem.
But there remain one or two items that require a word
or so more. It is true, as Galileo observed, that for ordinary bodies on the earth (which may be considered
as revolving in a large elliptic orbit at an average distance from the sun of about 93 million miles), the situation is very much like being on something that is moving
in a straight line, and there *is* an indifference to uniform
rectilinear motion and to rest so far as all the dynamical
problems are concerned. On the rotating earth, where
the arc during any time interval such as the flight of a
bullet is a part of a "circle" smaller than the annual

orbit, another Newtonian kind of principle can be invoked, the principle of the conservation of angular momentum.

The angular momentum of a small object rotating in a circle (as a stone held on the top of a tower on a rotating earth) is given by the expression mvr where r is the radius of rotation, m the mass, and v the speed along the circle. The principle says that under a large variety of conditions (specifically, in all circumstances in which there is no external force of a special kind), the angular momentum remains constant.

An example may be given. A man stands on a whirling platform, with his arms outstretched and clutching a 10-pound weight in each hand. He is set whirling slowly on the turntable and then is told to bring his hands in toward his body along a horizontal plane so that he looks like Fig. 34. He finds that he spins faster

Fig. 34.

and faster. Stretching his arms out once again will slow him down. For anyone who has never seen such a demonstration before (it is a standard figure in ice skating) the first encounter can be quite startling. Now let us see why these changes occurred. The speed v with which the masses m held in his hands move around is

$$v = \frac{2\pi r}{t}$$

where t is the time for a complete rotation, during which each mass m moves through a circumference of a circle of radius r. At first the angular momentum is

$$mvr = m \times \frac{2\pi r}{t} \times r = \frac{2\pi m r^2}{t}.$$

But as the man brings his arms in to his chest he makes r very much smaller. If $\frac{2\pi m r^2}{t}$ is to keep the same value, as the law of conservation demands, then t must get smaller too, which means that the time for a revolution becomes smaller as r diminishes.

What has this to do with a stone falling from a tower? At the top of the tower the radius of rotation is $R + r$ where R is the radius of the earth and r the height of the tower. When the stone strikes the ground, the radius of rotation is R. Therefore, like the masses drawn inward by the whirling mass, the stone must be moving around in a smaller circle when at the base of the tower than at the top, and so will whirl more quickly. Far from being left behind, the stone, according to our theory, should get a little ahead of the tower. How great an effect is this? Since the problem depends on t, the time for a rotation through 360°, we can get a much better idea of the magnitude of the problem if we study the angular speed than if we consider some linear speed (as we did in Chapter 1). Look at the hands of a moving clock, paying particular attention to the hour hand. By how much does it appear to shift in, say, five minutes, which corresponds to dropping a ball from a much greater height than the Empire State Building? Not by any discernible degree. Now the rotation of the earth through 360° takes just twice as much time as a complete rotation of the hour hand (12 hours). Since in five minutes the angular motion or rotation of the hour hand is not discernible to the unaided eye, a motion that is twice as slow produces practically no effect. Except in problems of long-range artillery firing, analysis of the movements of the trade winds and other phenomena on a vastly larger scale than the fall of a stone, we may neglect the earth's rotation.

Such was the great Newtonian revolution, which altered the whole structure of science and, indeed, turned the course of Western civilization. How has it fared in the last 300 years? Is the Newtonian mechanics still true?

All too often the misleading statement is made that Relativity theory has shown classical dynamics to be false. Nothing could be further from the truth! Relativistic corrections apply to objects moving at speeds v for which the ratio v/c is a significant quantity, c being the speed of light, or 186,000 miles per second. At the speeds attained in linear accelerators, cyclotrons, and other devices for studying atomic and sub-atomic particles, it is no longer true that the mass m of a physical object remains constant. Rather, it is found that the mass in motion is given by the equation

$$m = \frac{m_0}{\sqrt{1 - v^2/c^2}}$$

where m is the mass of an object moving at a speed v relative to the observer and m_0 is the mass of that same object observed at rest. Along with this revision goes Albert Einstein's now familiar equation relating mass and energy, $E = mc^2$, and the denial of the validity of Newton's belief in an "absolute" space and an "absolute" time. Well then, might we agree with the new couplet added by J. C. Squire to the one of Pope's we have quoted?

> It did not last: the Devil howling "Ho,
> Let Einstein be," restored the status quo.

But for the whole range of problems discussed by Newton—the motion of stars, planets, moons, airplanes, automobiles, baseballs, rockets, and every other type of gross body—the speeds v attainable are such that v/c has to all intents and purposes the value zero and we can still apply Newtonian dynamics without correction. (There is one example of a failure of Newtonian physics: a very small error in predicting the advance of the perihelion of Mercury—40″ per century!—for which we need to invoke Relativity theory.) Hence for engineering and all physics except a portion of atomic and subatomic physics, it is still the Newtonian physics that explains occurrences in the external world.

While it is true that the Newtonian mechanics is still applicable in the range of phenomena for which it was intended, the student should not make the mistake of thinking that the framework in which the system originally was set is equally valid. Newton believed that there *was* a sense in which space and time were "absolute" physical entities. Any deep analysis of his writings shows how in his mind his discoveries depended on these "absolutes." To be sure, Newton was aware that clocks do not measure absolute time, but only local time, and that we deal in our experiments with local space rather than absolute space. Thus he actually developed not merely a law of gravitational force and a system of rules for computing the answers to problems in mechanics but constructed a complete system based on a world view.

Today, following the Michelson-Morley experiment and Relativity, that world view can no longer be considered a valid basis for physical science, and the Newtonian principles are considered to be only a special, though extremely important, case of a more general system.

Some scientists hold that one of the greatest validations of Newtonian physics has been the set of predictions concerning satellite motions; they have enabled man to launch into orbit a series of artificial moons and to predict what will happen to them out in space. This may be so, but to the historian the greatest achievement of Newtonian science must ever be the first full explanation of the universe on mechanical principles—one set of axioms and a law of universal gravitation that applied to all matter everywhere: on earth as in the heavens. Newton recognized that the one example in nature in which there is pure inertial motion going on and on and on without frictional or other interference to bring it to a halt is the orbital motion of moons and planets. And yet this is not a uniform or unchanging motion along a single straight line, but rather along a constantly changing straight line, because planetary motions are a compounding of inertial motion with a continuing falling away from it. To see that moons and planets exemplify pure inertial motion required the same genius necessary to realize that the planetary law could be generalized into a law of universal attraction for all matter and that the motion of the moon partakes of the motion of the falling apple.

In Newton's genius we see the full significance of both Galilean mechanics and Kepler's laws of planetary motion realized in the development of the inertial principles required for the Copernican-Keplerian universe. A great French mathematician, Joseph Louis Lagrange (1736–1813), best defined Newton's achievement. There is only one law of the universe, he said, and Newton discovered it. Newton did not develop modern dynamics all by himself but depended heavily on certain of his predecessors; the debt in no way lessens the magnitude of his achievement. It only emphasizes the importance of such men as Galileo and Kepler and Huygens, who were great enough to make significant contributions to the Newtonian enterprise. Above all, we may see in Newton's work the degree to which science is a collective and a cumulative activity and we may find in it the measure of the influence of an individual genius on the future of a co-operative scientific effort. In Newton's achievement we see how science advances by heroic exercises of the imagination rather than by patient collecting and sorting of myriads of individual facts. Who, after studying Newton's magnificent contribution to thought, could deny that pure science exemplifies the creative accomplishment of the human spirit at its pinnacle?

GUIDE TO FURTHER READING

GENERAL BACKGROUND

Asterisks designate works from which quotations have been taken, with the publishers' permission, for inclusion in this book.

Marshall Clagett, editor: *Critical Problems in the History of Science* (Madison: University of Wisconsin Press, 1959)

*Sir Thomas Little Heath: *Aristarchus of Samos, the Ancient Copernicus: a History of Greek Astronomy to Aristarchus* (Oxford: Clarendon Press, 1913)

O. Neugebauer: *The Exact Sciences in Antiquity* (Princeton: Princeton University Press, 1952)

J. L. E. Dreyer: *History of Planetary Systems from Thales to Kepler* (Cambridge: University Press, 1906)

Marshall Clagett: *Greek Science in Antiquity* (New York: Abelard-Schuman, 1955)

Herbert Butterfield: *The Origins of Modern Science* (New York: The Macmillan Company, ed. 2, 1957)

Alistair C. Crombie: *Medieval and Early Modern Science* (2 vols: Garden City, New York: Doubleday Anchor Books, 1959)

ASTRONOMY AND COSMOLOGY

Alexandre Koyré: *From the Closed World to the In-*

finite Universe (New York: Harper Torchbooks, 1958; original edition, Baltimore: Johns Hopkins Press, 1957)

Thomas S. Kuhn: *The Copernican Revolution: Planetary Astronomy in the Development of Western Thought* (Cambridge: Harvard University Press, 1957)

A. R. Hall: *The Scientific Revolution (1500–1800), The Formation of the Modern Scientific Attitude* (Boston: The Beacon Press, 1956; original edition, New York: Longmans, Green and Company, 1954). Esp. ch. III, IV, IX on astronomy and mechanics.

THE WORK OF COPERNICUS

Angus Armitage: *Copernicus, the Founder of Modern Astronomy* (New York: Thomas Yoseloff, 1957)

Edward Rosen: *Three Copernican Treatises* (New York: Columbia University Press, 1939). Contains translations of the *Commentariolus* of Copernicus and *Letter against Werner,* and Rheticus' *Narratio Prima,* with commentaries and introduction.

THE WORK OF GALILEO

Marjorie Nicolson: *Science and Imagination* (Ithaca: Great Seal Books, Cornell University Press, 1956). Deals with the effects of the telescope and of the "new astronomy" in general on the imagination and, especially, on English literature.

*Stillman Drake: *Discoveries and Opinions of Galileo* (Garden City, New York: Doubleday Anchor Books, 1957). Contains translations of Galileo's *Starry Messenger* (1610), *Letters on Sunspots* (1613), *Letter to the Grand Duchess Christina*

(1615), . . . with commentaries and introductions by the foremost living expert on Galileo.

*Galileo Galilei: *Dialogue Concerning the Two Chief World Systems—Ptolemaic and Copernican,* translated by Stillman Drake (Berkeley and Los Angeles: University of California Press, 1953), *Dialogue on the Great World Systems,* the Salusbury Translation (1661) revised and annotated by Giorgio de Santillana (Chicago: University of Chicago Press, 1953)

*Galileo Galilei: *Dialogues Concerning Two New Sciences,* translated from the Latin and Italian by Henry Crew and Alfonso de Salvio (New York: Dover Publications, no date; original edition, New York: The Macmillan Company, 1914). The title should be "Discourses and Mathematical Demonstrations concerning Two New Sciences (*Discorsi e dimostrazioni matematiche, intorno à due nuove scienze*), the *Dialogue* being the preceding work. At the beginning of "Third Day," p. 152, lines 6 ff. of the text should be altered from "I have discovered by experiment some properties . . ." to "I have discovered [*comperio*] some properties. . . ." *Caveat lector!*

Giorgio de Santillana: *The Crime of Galileo* (Chicago: University of Chicago Press, 1955)

Edward Rosen: *The Naming of the Telescope* (New York: Abelard-Schuman, 1947).

No biography of Galileo in English is recommended.

THE WORK OF KEPLER

Max Caspar: *Kepler,* translated by C. Doris Hellman Pepper (New York: Abelard-Schuman, 1960)

Gerald Holton: *Johannes Kepler's Universe: its physics and metaphysics, American Journal of Physics,*

Vol. 24 (1956), pp. 340–51.

There is no English translation of any major work of Kepler.

THE WORK OF NEWTON

E. N. da C. Andrade: *Sir Isaac Newton* (Garden City, New York: Doubleday Anchor Books, 1958)

I. Bernard Cohen: *Franklin and Newton, an inquiry into speculative Newtonian experimental science* (Philadelphia: American Philosophical Society, 1956)

Louis T. More: *Isaac Newton* (New York: Charles Scribner's Sons, 1934)

Isaac Newton: *Mathematical Principles of Natural Philosophy,* translated by Andrew Motte (1729), revised by Florian Cajori (Berkeley: University of California Press, 1934)

Isaac Newton: *Opticks, or a Treatise of the Reflections, Refractions, Inflections & Colours of Light* (1704, fourth edition 1730), reprinted with a foreword by Albert Einstein, an introduction by Sir Edmund Whittaker, a preface by I. Bernard Cohen, and an analytical table of contents prepared by Duane H. D. Roller (New York: Dover Publications, 1952)

Isaac Newton's Papers & Letters on Natural Philosophy, edited by I. Bernard Cohen and Robert E. Schofield (Cambridge: Harvard University Press, 1958)

ADDITIONAL READING AND SOURCES

*The Paradiso of Dante Alighieri, (London: The Temple Classics, J. M. Dent)

*M. R. Cohen and I. E. Drabkin: *Source Book in Greek Science,* (Cambridge: Harvard University Press)

*W. K. Guthrie: translation of Aristotle's *On the Heavens,* (Cambridge: Harvard University Press, Loeb Classical Lib. Div.)

*E. W. Webster: translation of Aristotle's *Meteorologica,* (Oxford: Clarendon Press)

*John F. Dobson and Selig Brodetsky: translation of "Preface and Book I" of Copernicus's *De Revolutionibus* (London: *Occasional Notes of the Royal Astronomical Society,* Royal Astronomical Society, Burlington House)

*Johannes Kepler: *The Harmonies of the World,* Great Books of the Western World (Chicago: Encyclopaedia Brittanica, Inc., 1952)

The Principal Works of Simon Stevin, Volume I, General Introduction, Mechanics, edited by E. J. Dijkstarhuis (Amsterdam: C. V. Swets and Zeitlinger, 1933)

Johann Kepler, 1571–1630 (Baltimore: Williams & Wilkins)

I. Bernard Cohen, *The Nature and Growth of the Physical Sciences, A Historical Introduction to Physics* (New York: John Wiley and Sons, in press)

INDEX